The Conduction of the Nervous Impulse

The Sherrington Lectures

In 1948, on the occasion of the ninetieth birthday of Sir Charles Scott Sherrington, O.M., G.B.E., M.D., F.R.S., the Council of the University resolved to institute a Lectureship in recognition of his distinguished contributions to Physiology and Medicine and of his association with the University of Liverpool as George Holt Professor of Physiology from 1895 to 1913.

The appointment to the Sherrington Lectureship is made biennially by the Council of the University on the joint recommendation of the Faculties of Medicine and Science.

The following lectures have been delivered and are published by Liverpool University Press:

The Sherrington Lectures VII

The Conduction of the
Nervous Impulse

A. L. Hodgkin Sc.D., F.R.S.

Foulerton Research Professor of the Royal Society
University of Cambridge

LIVERPOOL UNIVERSITY PRESS 1965

591.18
H 689 c
10 9955

Preface

In March 1961 I had the honour to give the Sherrington Lectures in the University of Liverpool. At Professor Gregory's suggestion I talked mainly about experiments on which my colleagues and I had been engaged in the immediate past. In writing up the lectures I have included some additional information in order to give a background to the more recent work. This has been taken partly from a lecture published by the Royal Society in 1958 and partly from other, unpublished lectures given during the last few years.

For permission to reproduce figures, I am indebted to the authors mentioned in the legends and to the editors of the following journals: *J. Physiol.*, *J. gen. Physiol.*, *J. cell. comp. Physiol.*, *Amer. J. Physiol.*, *J. biophys. biochem. Cytol.*, *Proc. Roy. Soc.*, *Nature*, *Arch. Sci. Physiol.*, *Rev. modern Physics*, *Scientific American* and the *Handbook of Physiology*. My thanks are also due to several colleagues for reading the manuscript, and to Miss S. Elton for her help with the bibliography and index.

A. L. H.

Contents

7

Illustrations

8

9

CHAPTER I

The method of signalling in the nervous system

My aim in these lectures is to give some idea of the mechanism which enables nerve fibres to carry messages about the bodies of man and animals. I shall try to do this by considering specific experiments rather than by attempting to summarize the vast amount of information which has accumulated during the last 150 years. Much of the recent evidence has been obtained on giant nerve fibres, particularly those of squids and cuttlefish. Now the squid is a very distant relation – our last common ancestor, of whose form we are totally ignorant, has been dead for several hundred million years – and you may wonder whether information obtained from its nerves is of much interest to human physiologists. However, it turns out that all nervous messages have certain features in common and that results obtained on one preparation can often be applied in a fairly general manner. If further justification is required all that need be done is to draw attention to the advantages of working with single nerve fibres and to the great difficulty of making physical or chemical measurements if, as in mammals, the largest fibres are only one fiftieth of a millimeter in diameter.

Before embarking on recent work it is worth mentioning some familiar aspects of nervous activity. Two facts were learnt at a very early stage. In the first place, it was found that some animals were able to produce electricity and, in the second, that nerves or muscles could be stimulated by electric shocks. Both points were clearly established by the end of the eighteenth century but something was known long before that. Many fish produce electrical pulses and in some species, *Torpedo*, *Electrophorus* and *Malapterurus*, these are large enough to be painful to human beings or lethal to small animals. A fifth-dynasty Egyptian mural[1] in a tomb at Sakkara (*c* 2600 B.C.) contains a clear representation of *Malapterurus*, the electric catfish, and D'Arcy Thompson in his book on Greek Fishes mentions many references to the painful effects of the discharges of *Torpedo*. It is amusing to read that as early as the first century A.D. a Roman physician, Scribonius, should have recommended the discharge of the *Torpedo* as a cure for gout, headaches and epilepsy. No recent physician seems to have used

1. Fritsch 1887, Steindorff 1913.

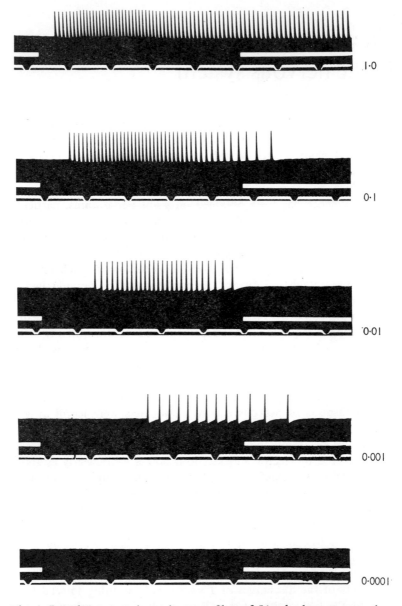

Fig. 1. Impulses set up in optic nerve fibre of *Limulus* by one second flash of light with relative intensities shown at right. The lower white line marks 0·2 second intervals and the gap in the upper white line gives the period for which the eye was illuminated. (From Hartline, 1934.)

electric treatment for gout, but as Dr Fulton pointed out in his Sher-rington Lecture, the prescription for headaches and epilepsy is reminis-cent of modern shock therapy.

By the end of the eighteenth century a good deal was known about electric fish and Volta (1800) compared his electric battery to the stack of plates in an electric fish. Indeed he refers to his pile of cells as an artificial electric organ. Nowadays people take electric batteries for granted and think it clever of electric fish to have achieved the same end with the limited means at their disposal. But the fish is clearly the innovator and man the unconscious plagiarist. A similar situation has arisen in connection with modern views about 'feed-back' in engineer-ing and biology. The idea of reflex-control by proprioceptors in muscle was developed by Sherrington long before engineers started to include devices for measuring rate or position in their servo-mechanisms. And the same general notion is implicit in Claude Bernard's concept of the fixity of the internal environment.

The study of electric fish showed that animals produce electricity, but the discovery of the action currents of nerve and muscle had to wait for the development of suitable recording instruments. Here I shall not consider the historical aspect but will go straight to our own period. As a result of the investigations of Gotch, Sherrington's pre-decessor at Liverpool, and of Keith Lucas and Adrian at Cambridge, we have learnt that nervous activity is invariably accompanied by electrical changes. When a sense organ is active or when the brain issues an order, impulses can be detected in the appropriate nerve fibre. Figure 1, which is taken from a paper by Hartline (1934) shows the sensory impulses set up by stimulating the eye of *Limulus* with a 1-second flash of light of different intensities. It can be seen that the response consists of a train of identical impulses and that the frequency increases with the intensity of the light. A similar type of experiment, Figure 2, gives the response of a mammalian stretch receptor (Mat-thews 1933) and Figure 3 illustrates the regular groups of motor im-pulses which cause the rhythmical contractions of the respiratory muscles (Bronk and Ferguson, 1935).

Experiments such as these prove that the nervous impulse in one fibre is of constant amplitude and shape and that its characteristics cannot be altered by changing the strength or the quality of the stimulus. The inference is that the intensity of a sensation or a movement is con-trolled by varying the frequency of impulses and the number of fibres in action. The quality of a sensation does not depend upon changes in individual messages but upon alterations in the type of nerve fibres which are active. Although there are complications when the nature of

13

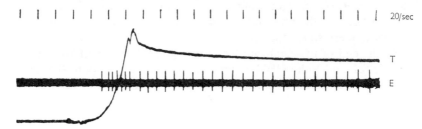

Fig. 2. Impulses set up by stretching cat's soleus muscle to a final tension of 260 grams. Time marker: 0·05 sec. T, tension; E, electric response of nerve with impulses recorded diphasically. The response is from a B type nerve ending located in the tendon. (From Matthews, 1933.)

Fig. 3. Groups of impulses in a single motor nerve fibre to an external intercostal muscle in the cat. Time marker: 0·2 sec. Lower line, respiration with upward movement indicating inspiration. (From Bronk & Ferguson, 1935.)

sensations are examined in detail it is roughly true to say that there are separate fibres for each class of sensation. In recent years some physiologists have questioned the validity of the idea of specific nerve fibres, particularly in relation to skin sensation.[1] However, although the division of sensations may be more complicated than was formerly thought there is no doubt at all about the proposition that the impulse does not change with the nature or strength of the stimulus. In a single fibre each impulse is invariant, and in these lectures, which are concerned with the mechanism of conduction rather than with the nature of sensation, that is all we need to keep in mind.

The invariance of the action potential arises because the energy used in propagation does not come from the stimulus but is released by the nerve fibre along its length. In this respect nervous conduction resembles the burning of a fuse of gunpowder and is unlike the propagation of an electric signal along a cable. The basic unit of information is the action potential which lasts about 1/1000 second and which travels at a velocity of 1–100 metres per second, the speed depending on the fibre diameter,[2] temperature and on whether or not the fibre is myelinated (Table 1).

1. Weddell, Palmer & Pallie, 1955.   2. Erlanger & Gasser, 1937.

Table 1. Conduction Velocities in Nerve and Muscle

Tissue	Temperature °C	Myelinated (M) or unmyelinated (U)	Fibre Diameter μ	Velocity m/sec.	Notes
Cat myelinated nerve fibres	38	M	2–20	10–100	a
Cat unmyelinated nerve fibres	38	U	0·3–1·3	0·7–2·3	a
Frog myelinated nerve fibres	24	M	3–16	6–32	b
Prawn myelinated nerve fibres	20	M	35	20	c
Crab large nerve fibres	20	U	30	5	d
Squid giant axon	20	U	500	25	d
Frog muscle fibre	20	U	60	1·6	d

(a) References, particularly Hursh (1939) in Patton (1960).
(b) Tasaki (1953).
(c) Holmes, Pumphrey & Young (1942).
(d) References and data in Katz (1948).
For myelinated fibres the figure given is the external diameter of the myelin.

Although nerves normally conduct impulses in one direction – towards the central nervous system in sensory fibres, away from it in motor fibres – all nerves can conduct impulses in both directions and the velocity at which the impulse propagates is independent of the direction in which it is travelling.

If an electrical engineer were to look at the nervous system he would see at once that signalling electrical information along nerve fibres is a formidable problem. In our nerves the diameter of the axis cylinder varies between about $0·1\mu$ and 10μ. The inside of the fibre contains ions and is a reasonably good conductor of electricity. However, the fibre is so small that its longitudinal resistance is exceedingly high. A simple calculation shows that in a 1μ fibre containing axoplasm with a resistivity of 100 ohm cm, the resistance per unit length is about 10^{10} ohms per cm. This means that the electrical resistance of a metre's length of small nerve fibre is about the same as that of 10^{10} miles of 22 gauge copper wire, the distance being roughly ten times that between the earth and the planet Saturn. An electrical engineer would find himself in

15

great difficulties if he were asked to wire up the solar system using ordinary cables. He might solve the problem by using repeating units which reinforced the signal as it travelled along the cable. But in this case the energy for conveying the signal would have to be fed into the cable at various points along its length and the system would begin to approximate more closely to that found in a nerve fibre. The all-or-nothing mode of conduction would seem to be a convenient way of

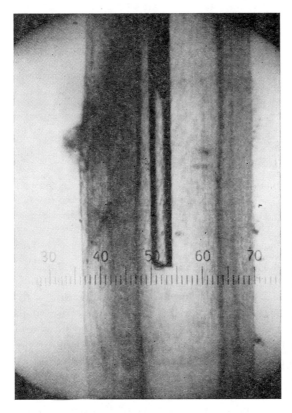

Fig. 4. Photomicrograph of a recording electrode inside a giant axon of a squid. The giant axon, which shows as a clear space, was left with small nerve fibres on either side; one scale division equals 33μ. (From Hodgkin & Huxley, 1939.)

overcoming the difficulty imposed by the high longitudinal resistance of a small cylinder of protoplasm. It may also be important in eliminating the disturbing effects of thermal noise. With a large nerve fibre, in which the electrical resistance between a point inside and outside the fibre is relatively low, electrical fluctuations resulting from thermal noise are very small compared to the action potential. But they might be appreciable in small fibres and could lead to mistakes if the precise form of the message determined the quality of a sensation. This source of confusion is eliminated in a system in which an all-or-nothing action potential is the basic unit of information and quality depends on the type of fibre which transmits the message.

General nature of the action potential

Many years before the introduction of the microelectrode technique physiologists believed that the electrical changes associated with the activity of nerve and muscle arose at the surface membrane. This idea

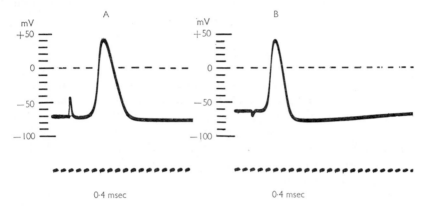

Fig. 5. Action potentials in intact (A) and isolated axon (B) of squid. Time marks: 0·4 msec apart. Temperature 8·5° C, record A; 12·5° C, record B. (Hodgkin & Keynes quoted by Hodgkin, 1958.)

was verified by experiments in which the electrical potential difference across the surface of the fibre was measured directly with an internal electrode. The earliest experiments with nerve were made with the giant axon of the squid, *Loligo*.[1] Here, the usual method is to introduce a long capillary electrode into one end of the fibre and push it in for a distance of 10–30 mm. (Fig. 4). The presence of an internal electrode does not have any obvious effect on the activity of the nerve, since impaled axons survive for many hours and the external action potential is not altered by the insertion of an internal electrode. Another method which has a wide application depends on the fact that a very small capillary can be inserted transversely into many types of fibre without causing appreciable damage (Ling & Gerard, 1949). As a rule such electrodes have tip diameters of less than 0.5μ and are filled with 3 molar KCl[2] in order to reduce their electrical resistance. Both methods have been applied to the giant axons of *Loligo* and give similar results. In such experiments it is found that the inside of a resting nerve fibre is 50 to 70 mV

1. Curtis & Cole, 1940, 1942; Hodgkin & Huxley, 1939, 1945.
2. Nastuk & Hodgkin, 1950.

negative to the external solution; this standing difference in electrical potential is known as the resting potential. When an impulse travels along the fibre, the inside swings momentarily positive giving a transient action potential with an amplitude of 100–120 mV. At the crest of the action potential the inside of the fibre is 40–50 mV positive to the external solution.

Figure 5 illustrates the form of the action potential in the giant axon of *Loligo*. The record on the left is from an intact axon in its natural position in the animal. When the microelectrode which had a tip diameter of about 0.5μ, was pushed through the surface, the potential jumped suddenly to a new value about 70 mV negative to the zero – this is the resting potential. The record shows the action potential which travels along the fibre, its amplitude is 110 mV and duration (at $9°$ C) about 1.5 millisecond. In this experiment the squid had been subjected to only slight operative procedure and the nerve was still connected to the muscles. A few milliseconds after the impulse had passed the microelectrode it reached the muscles. The body wall then gave a powerful flap which smashed the microelectrode and terminated the experiment. For this and many other reasons it is simpler to work with an isolated axon as has been done in obtaining the record in Figure 5B. The action potential differs slightly from that in the intact animal but the essential features of the conduction mechanism are the same in both cases.

The duration of the action potential increase 2–3 fold for a fall in temperature of $10°$ C. In frog fibres at $20°$ C the duration is about 1 millisecond and in mammalian fibres about 0.5 millisecond at $38°$ C.

When a brief electrical current is applied to a nerve it is found that the impulse always arises at the cathode. This means that the event which starts the impulse is a decrease of the electrical potential difference across the membrane. The amount by which the potential difference must be reduced varies with the concentration of divalent ions (Ca and Mg) in the external medium, and with a normal medium is about 15 mV in squid or frog nerve.

Shortly after a stimulus has set up an impulse the nerve enters an absolute refractory period during which no stimulus, however strong, can evoke a second response. The absolute refractory period has about the same duration as the main part of the action potential and is followed by a relative refractory period during which a second impulse can be evoked but only by a stimulus which is stronger than normal.

Another interesting characteristic of nerve fibres is the maximum frequency at which they can transmit impulses. It might be thought that the minimum interval between impulses in a train would be equal to the absolute refractory period. However, this is not correct because the impulse travels more slowly in the relative refractory period and also because an appreciable time is required to launch an impulse into refractory nerve. This means that the interval in a continuous train must be greater than the absolute refractory period. If the interval between shocks is equal to the absolute refractory period two impulses can be launched but the third will fail. *Carcinus* nerve fibres, which have an absolute refractory period of about 1 millisecond at 20° c, cannot transmit higher frequencies than about 500/sec.[1] Mammalian fibres with an absolute refractory period of about 0·5 millisecond have an upper limit of about 1000/sec.[2] These rates are much higher than those normally encountered in the living animal. The auditory nerve may sometimes fire at 1000/sec but other mammalian sense organs or motor neurones rarely send off impulses at rates greater than 200/sec. The normal working range in the body is 5–100 impulses/sec.

Examples of animals which make full use of the ability of nerves to carry impulses at a high frequency are to be found amongst the Gymnotid electric fish of South America. These animals find their way about and capture prey in muddy water by emitting electrical pulses and detecting disturbances in the electric field with sensory receptors (about which very little is known). The discharge of the electric organ apparently goes on continuously throughout life and in some species may be as high as 1600/sec.[3] Since each electrical pulse is started by a nerve impulse, the nerve fibres as well as the electroplates, must be capable of carrying impulses at this rate without intermission. Assuming that a fish such as *Stenarchus albifrons*,[3] which emits pulses at 1000/sec, does so continuously for three years the nerve fibres and electroplates must in their life-time carry 10^{11} impulses.

1. Hodgkin, 1938.   2. Gasser & Grundfest, 1936.
3. Lissmann, 1961.

CHAPTER II

Structure and general properties
of nerve fibres

On the basis of their appearance under the microscope nerve fibres
may be divided into two classes. In the myelinated nerve fibres which,
in vertebrates, include all except the smallest axons, the protoplasmic
core of the fibre is surrounded by a sheath of fatty material known as
myelin. The sheath is interrupted at intervals of about a millimetre by
short gaps called nodes of Ranvier (Fig. 6). In unmyelinated fibres
there is no fatty sheath and the fibre consists of a cylinder of protoplasm separated from the external medium by a membrane whose
thickness is about 100Å. A similar membrane is present at the node of
Ranvier. In the peripheral fibres of higher animals the axon is partially
enclosed by a Schwann cell or by a layer of Schwann cells about which
more will be said later. The length of nerve fibres varies from a fraction
of a millimetre in a small insect to several metres in a large mammal.
The diameter is usually between 0·1 and 20μ but certain invertebrates
have very large unmyelinated axons and, as J. Z. Young[1] discovered,
those in the squid may be as much as 1 mm in diameter.

The nucleus of a nerve fibre is in the cell body which in a typical
vertebrate fibre is located either in the dorsal root ganglion (sensory
fibres) or in the ventral horn of the spinal cord (motor fibres). The
nucleus and cell body are essential for the growth and continued existence of nerve fibres but not for the conduction of impulses. Thus frog
nerves will continue to conduct impulses for a week or more after they
have been separated from their cell bodies, and isolated squid axons
survive for 24 hours after they have been removed from the animal.
Although the giant axon of a squid behaves like a single cell, each fibre
is in fact a syncytium formed by the fusion of a large number of fibres
and a single giant axon is connected to several hundred cell bodies in
the stellate ganglion.[2]

When viewed under a low-power objective in the light microscope a
giant axon appears as a transparent cylinder of protoplasm surrounded
by a thin sheath of connective tissue (Fig. 7). This sheath is considered
to have no specific function other than that of providing mechanical
support for the axon itself. In the fresh state, the protoplasm in squid

1. Young, 1936a, b.   2. Young, 1936a.

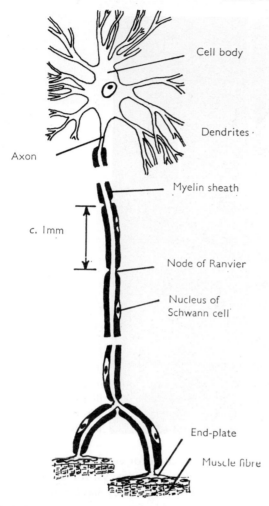

Cell body

Dendrites ·

Axon

Myelin sheath

c. 1mm

Node of Ranvier

Nucleus of
Schwann cell

End-plate

Muscle fibre

Fig. 6. Diagram show-
ing some of the main
structures in a motor
nerve fibre of a verte-
brate. (After Katz, 1961.)

axons appears to be a gel and if a glass capillary which has been
inserted into the protoplasm is withdrawn it leaves a fluid space down
which particles can be seen to fall under the influence of gravity. When
the particles reach the end of the hole drilled by the capillary they come
to rest showing that the protoplasm behaves like a solid rather than a
liquid. The protoplasm of a giant axon has a weak birefringence of a
kind consistent with axially orientated protein micelles[1] and longitudinal neurofibrils are often seen in stained preparations. However, as
will appear in the next chapter, there are strong reasons for believing

1. Bear, Schmitt & Young, 1937.

21

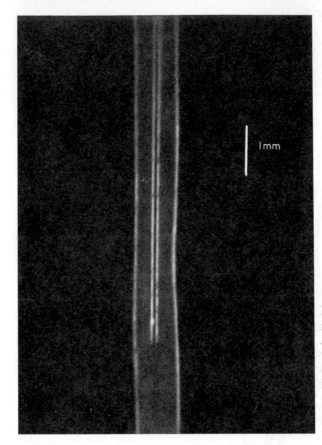

Fig. 7. Cleaned giant axon of *Loligo*, with glass tube 0·1 mm in diameter, inside it; dark ground illumination. (FromHodgkin Keynes, 1956.)

that the bulk of the axoplasm is not essential for conduction and that, whatever the importance of neurofibrils in other ways, for instance in controlling the growth pattern of nerve fibres, they have little to do with the chain of events directly responsible for nervous conduction. Mitochondria have been seen in the protoplasm of all nerve fibres examined and in the large nerve fibres of crustacea they are concentrated in a ring just below the surface membrane,[1] an arrangement well-suited to supplying energy to the membrane.

One of the exciting things which has happened during the last ten years is that electronmicroscopists have begun to 'see' the cell membranes about which biologists have speculated for so many years. Quotation marks are used with the word *see* because of course the membrane is not seen in the ordinary sense. What is visualized is the

1. Geren & Schmitt, 1954.

electron stain, osmic acid, permanganate or phosphotungstate as the case may be. However, this is not very different from ordinary histology, for most sections would be invisible without some kind of stain. A full account of recent advances in this field has been given by Robert-

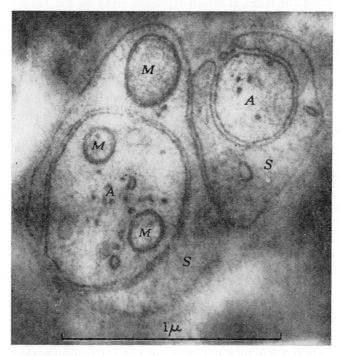

Fig. 8. Electromicrograph of two small unmyelinated axons from the frog's sciatic nerve fixed with permanganate. A–axon. S–Schwann cell. M–mitochondrion. (Robertson, 1957.)

son (1960a) and his articles should be consulted by anyone interested in pursuing the subject.

Figure 8 is a reproduction of an electronmicrograph of two small unmyelinated axons from the frog. It shows the axis cylinder, the axon membrane and the Schwann cell which surrounds but does not completely enclose the axon. The total thickness of the axon membrane is about 70Å; if examined under high power the membrane can be resolved into two dense lines about 50Å apart. Robertson suggests that the electron stain is deposited on either side of a bimolecular layer of lipid, possibly on the polar groups or proteins on either side of a hydrocarbon layer.

As yet no fine structure has been seen in the membrane, and although it is reassuring to know that there is a membrane with about the thickness predicted from electrical measurements, electronmicroscopy has not reached the stage at which it throws light on the nature of the permeability changes. The most interesting thing that has come out of electronmicroscopical studies of nerve is in connection with the Schwann cell. Figure 9A illustrates the simplest situation in which a single Schwann cell encloses a single axon. Frequently, as in the Remak bundles of vertebrates, several axons share one Schwann cell giving an arrangement like that in Figure 9B. You meet the opposite situation in the larger axons of crustacea where there are several Schwann cells round the perimeter of one axon (Fig. 9C). In the squid giant axon there is an even more complicated arrangement with several layers of Schwann cell processes overlapping one another (9D). However, the fibre is never totally enclosed by the Schwann cells and one can always find channels connecting the axon membrane with the outside world. Since the potassium ions which move outwards during the impulse have to pass through the Schwann cell layer one might expect that they would pile up immediately outside the membrane when the fibre is stimulated at a high frequency. Frankenhaeuser and I observed effects which we explained in this way and calculated that the aqueous space immediately outside the axon membrane was 150-300Å thick;[1] electronmicroscopists usually give the width of the space between the axon and Schwann cell as 150Å.

Since all peripheral nerve fibres in higher animals are surrounded by Schwann cells it is natural to inquire into the reason for the association. It seems rather unlikely that they are connected with conduction in any very direct manner. There is no Schwann cell layer in muscle fibres, yet these conduct an action potential not unlike that found in nerve. It has been suggested that the Schwann cells might have something to do with transporting ions during recovery. However, this does not fit with experiments which suggest that, after poisoning with cyanide, ion pumping can be restored by ATP inside but not outside the axon membrane (Chapter VI). A more probable explanation is that the nucleated Schwann cells are involved in synthesizing enzymes or membrane components which the nerve fibre cannot manufacture. Muscle fibres which are nucleated can carry out their own maintenance and do not need a Schwann cell. Some years ago Geren and Schmitt (1954) suggested that the mitochondria in nerve fibres might be formed from invaginations

1. Frankenhaeuser & Hodgkin, 1956.

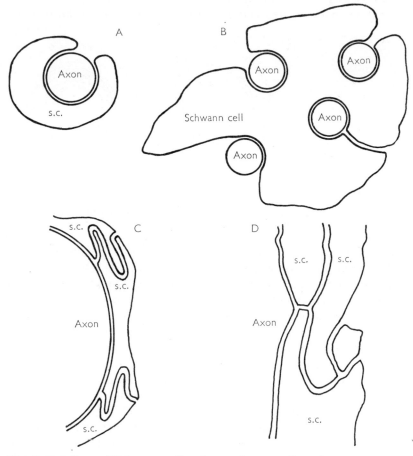

Fig. 9. Relations of Schwann cell and axon in unmyelinated axons.

A. Small unmyelinated axon with one Schwann cell (S.C.).
B. Remak bundle; several unmyelinated axons share one Schwann cell.
C. Medium sized crustacean axon with several Schwann cells round one axon.
D. Giant axon of *Loligo*; many overlapping Schwann cell processes form a complex layer.

A & B are based on Robertson, 1960a; C on an unpublished photograph taken by P. F. Baker; D on Geren & Schmitt, 1954. The Schwann cell layer in the squid axon is usually thicker and more complicated than shown here.

Note that in this figure the cell membrane is represented by a single line whereas in Figs. 10 and 11 it is represented by two lines.

of the Schwann cell. Electronmicrographs certainly show such invaginations but as Geren and Schmitt recognized there is no real evi-

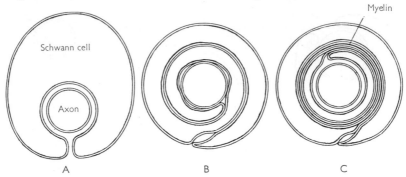

Fig. 10. Diagram illustrating formation of myelin by Schwann cell on Geren's theory. (Robertson, 1958.)

dence that they form mitochondria. Yet another possibility, again unsupported by experiment, is that the Schwann cell layer could increase conduction velocity in a manner analogous to the myelin sheath. However, the difficulty here is that nothing equivalent to a node of Ranvier has been described. For the time being, the function of the Schwann cell must be regarded as unknown but it is reasonable to suggest that we may set this aspect aside without missing any essential part of the conduction mechanism.

In myelinated nerve fibres the Schwann cell has the interesting and important function of manufacturing the myelin sheath. As will appear in the next chapter myelin is an insulator which enables the action potential to skip from one node of Ranvier to the next. The insulation probably consists of layers of lipid with protein sandwiched between them; the distance between the lipid layers is about 85Å. By studying developing chick embryos, Geren (1954) showed that the Schwann cell laid down myelin by spiralling round the axon and that the individual layers in myelin were continuous with the membrane of the Schwann cell. Figure 10 illustrates the mechanism. After completing a few turns, the cytoplasm of the Schwann cell disappears leaving the insulating membranes piled on top of one another (Fig. 11). A difference between the cytoplasmic and external face of the Schwann cell membrane probably accounts for the alternation of dense and less dense lines seen in electronmicrographs and for the total repeat distance of 170Å found by the method of X-ray diffraction.[1] There seems to be no preferred direction of winding on the insulation, both clockwise and anticlock-

1. Robertson, 1960a; Schmitt & Geschwind, 1957.

wise spirals occurring in a more or less random manner in different internodes of the same fibre.[1]

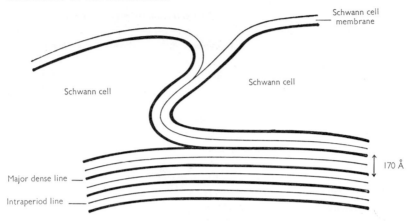

Fig. 11. Diagram of outer edge of myelin sheath showing probable origin of lines of alternating density seen in electronmicrographs. (After Schmitt, 1959.)

Some physicochemical properties of nerve fibres

One of the many useful properties of giant nerve fibres is that samples of protoplasm or axoplasm as it is usually called can be obtained by squeezing out the contents from a cut end. Table 2 gives some of the results obtained from chemical analysis of axoplasm. As in many other cells there is a high concentration of potassium ions and a relatively low concentration of sodium and chloride ions. This is the reverse of the situation in the animals' blood or in sea water, where sodium and chloride are the dominant ions and potassium is relatively dilute. Potassium ions are probably free inside the fibre and do not seem to be bound to proteins or other large molecules. This statement is based on evidence from a variety of experiments. In the first place it would be difficult to account for the high electrical conductivity of axoplasm (0·5–0·8 times sea water) or for osmotic balance unless the main ionic constituents of the protoplasm were free. Electrical measurements which show that the membrane behaves like a potassium electrode at high external concentrations of potassium[2] also require that the internal activity coefficient of potassium be similar to that in the external solution. More direct evidence is provided by studies with radioactive potassium, [42]K, which show that the mobility and diffusion coefficient of this ion is nearly the same as in free solution[3] and by experiments

1. Robertson, 1960b.
2. Curtis & Cole, 1942; Huxley & Stämpfli, 1951b; Hodgkin & Keynes, 1955b; R. H. Adrian, 1956.　　　　3. Hodgkin & Keynes, 1953.

27

Table 2. Concentrations of Ions and Other Substances in Freshly Isolated Axons of *Loligo*.

Substance	Concentration ($mmole/kg$ H_2O)		
	Axoplasm	Blood	Sea water
K	400	20	10
Na	50	440	460
Cl	40–150	560	540
Ca	0·4	10	10
Mg	10	54	53
Isethionate	250	—	—
Aspartate	75	—	—
Glutamate	12	—	—
Succinate + fumarate	17	—	—
Orthophosphate	2·5–9	—	—
ATP	0·7–1·7	—	—
Arginine phosphate	1·8–5·7	—	—
Water	865 g/kg.	870 g/kg	966 g/kg

For references and notes see Hodgkin, 1958; principal authors are Koechlin, 1955; Steinbach, 1941; Steinbach & Spiegelman, 1943; Keynes & Lewis, 1956, and Caldwell, 1956, 1960.

with internal potassium electrodes which give an activity coefficient similar to that in sea water.[1]

Although there is little doubt that the potassium inside nerve fibres is mainly in the ionized form, caution should be exercised in applying this result to other ions which have a greater tendency to form complexes. Measurements of the mobility of calcium inside squid axons show that this ion moves in an electric field at a rate less than 1/30 of that in free solution[2] and Hinke's observations with Na- and K-electrodes suggest that the activity coefficient of sodium in axoplasm is about 30 per cent less than that of potassium.[3]

The excess of potassium inside the fibre is balanced by organic anions of which, in squid fibres, isethionic acid was shown by Koechlin (1955) to be the most important. Other substances which help to balance the cations are aspartic acid and phosphate esters such as arginine phosphate and ATP. Isethionic acid has so far been found only in cephalopod nerve; in many excitable tissues it is not known what anions balance the high concentration of potassium.[4]

1. Hinke, 1961.   2. Hodgkin & Keynes, 1957.   3. Hinke, 1961.
    4. For the balance sheet in vertebrate muscle see Conway, 1957, and in crustacean nerve see Lewis, 1952.

At the surface of the nerve fibre the membrane acts as a barrier and prevents the ions in the external solution from mixing rapidly with the internal solution. This membrane has a high electrical resistance, about 1000 ohm cm^2 in a resting axon of *Loligo*,[1] and an electrical capacity[2] of about 1 microfarad/cm^2. These are values which might be expected from a bimolecular layer of lipid with a thickness of 50Å, a dielectric constant of 5 and an electrical resistivity of 2 $\times$ 10^9 ohm cm. The high resistivity of the membrane is in striking contrast to that of the axoplasm and external fluid, these being about 30 and 20 ohm cm respectively. During a nerve impulse the conductivity of the membrane increases about 100 fold and sodium and potassium ions move down their concentration gradients. These movements are thought to provide the immediate source of energy for conducting the impulse and will be considered further in later chapters.

Little is known about the chemistry of the nerve membrane but it is generally believed to contain both lipids and proteins. As we have seen, the myelin sheath is formed from many layers of the membranes of Schwann cells; analysis of the sheath therefore gives us some idea of the chemical compostion of cell membranes. Myelin consists of proteins, lipoproteins and lipids; the principal lipids being cholesterol, cerebrosides and numerous phospholipids of which lecithin, cephalin and phosphatydyl-serine are some of the simplest.[3] The lipids usually have long paraffin chains attached to a polar group and it is natural to suppose that the cell membrane may be a bimolecular leaflet with nonpolar groups in the middle and polar groups at the edges. A structure of this kind was first proposed by Gorter and Grendel (1925) and was elaborated by Davson and Danielli (1943) who suggested that the polar groups of the lipid were in contact with protein monolayers on either side of the membrane. The only other preparation on which much direct evidence about the chemistry of cell membranes has been obtained is in the red cell. Here analysis of the 'ghosts' produced by allowing red cells to burst in dilute solutions gives information about the chemistry of the membrane. It is found that the ratio of lipid to protein is about 1:1·7 and that there is enough lipid to make a layer 30Å thick. Some of the principal lipids are cholesterol, 30 per cent, lecithin, 11 per cent, cephalin, 46 per cent, and sphingomyelin 8 per cent.[4]

1. Cole & Hodgkin, 1939.
2. Curtis & Cole, 1938.
3. Finean, 1957, gives the molecular ratios of cholesterol, phospholipid and cerebroside as 2:2:1.
4. Parpart & Ballantine, 1952.

CHAPTER III

The membrane theory of nervous conduction

At the beginning of this century, Bernstein published his membrane theory of nervous conduction.[1] He adopted Hermann's idea that propagation depended on a flow of electric current in a cable-like structure[2] but added suggestions about the way in which the resting potential and action potential originate. Since the action potential involves a reversal of membrane potential and is not simply a neutralization as Bernstein supposed, his theory has had to be modified in one important respect. But in broad outline it has stood the test of time better than most biological theories and the underlying assumptions about the role of the membrane, which probably seemed speculative to Bernstein's contemporaries, would now be accepted without question by the majority of electrophysiologists. Apart from mentioning Overton's remarkable paper[3] on the part played by sodium ions, which appeared in the same volume of *Pflüger's Archiv* as Bernstein's article, I shall not attempt to trace the historical development of the subject but will outline the membrane theory as it stands today.

A nerve fibre is regarded as a long cylinder with a conducting core and a surface membrane of relatively high resistance. In the resting state the membrane is assumed to be more permeable to potassium than to sodium ions. Since potassium ions are more concentrated inside the fibre they tend to set up a potential difference with the inside negative and the outside positive. If the membrane were permeable to potassium ions alone, the potential difference across it would approach that given by the Nernst equation for a potassium electrode, i.e.

$$V_K = \frac{RT}{F} \ln \frac{[K]_o}{[K]_i} \tag{1}$$

where V_K is the equilibrium potential of the potassium ion defined in the sense internal potential minus external potential, $[K]_o$ and $[K]_i$ are the potassium concentrations (or strictly activities) outside and inside the fibre, R is the gas constant, T the absolute temperature and F the Faraday. With potassium concentrations similar to those found in

1. Bernstein, 1902, 1912.   2. Hermann, 1899.   3. Overton, 1902.

squid blood (20 mM) and axoplasm (400 mM), the value predicted for V_K is -75 mV. Resting potentials of about 70 mV have been observed in intact axons with natural circulation[1]. The smaller resting potentials obtained from isolated axons immersed in sea water are probably explained by less perfect discrimination between K and Na, the permeability ratio between K and Na under these conditions being of the order of 10:1. One of the main pieces of evidence for regarding the resting potential as at least partly due to the potassium concentration cell is that at high external potassium concentrations the membrane behaves like a potassium electrode.[2]

In order to explain the reversal of membrane potential during the impulse it is assumed that at the crest of the spike the membrane is selectively permeable to the sodium ion. For a membrane permeable to sodium ions alone the Nernst formula

$$V_{Na} = \frac{RT}{F} \ln \frac{[Na]_o}{[Na]_i} \qquad (2)$$

gives a limiting value of $+55$ mV for concentration ratio of 9. This is somewhat larger than the reversed potential observed experimentally – as would be expected if the active membrane is not completely selective for sodium. The assumption is supported by the observation that the action potential of many excitable tissues fails in the absence of external sodium or lithium and that the reversed potential difference across the membrane varies with external sodium concentration in the manner predicted by equation 2.[3] Hinke's measurements with an internal sodium electrode also provide strong evidence for the validity of the assumption in the giant nerve fibre of *Loligo*.[4]

Propagation is brought about by the flow of current between resting and active nerve. The upper part of Figure 12 illustrates the flow of current in an unmyelinated axon of which the squid giant fibre is an example. Suppose that point A is active and point B is resting. A is sodium permeable so the inside of the fibre is positive; B is potassium permeable so the inside is negative. Electric current therefore flows in a local circuit between resting and active nerve. This current reduces the membrane potential just ahead of the active region by drawing charge out of the membrane's capacity. As a result of the decrease in membrane potential the permeability to sodium rises and sodium ions enter, making the inside of the fibre electrically positive. In this way a wave of

1. See Hodgkin, 1958; Moore & Cole, 1960
2. References in footnote 2, p. 27.
3. Hodgkin & Katz, 1949; Nastuk & Hodgkin, 1950; Huxley & Stämpfli, 1951b; Draper & Weidmann, 1951; Cole, 1955; Dalton, 1958.
4. Hinke, 1961.

internal positivity and of increased sodium permeability spreads along the nerve fibre. The propagating agent is the electric current which is generated by the change in permeability.

If the model which has just been described could be made it would be found to give a step-like action potential of infinite duration; such a

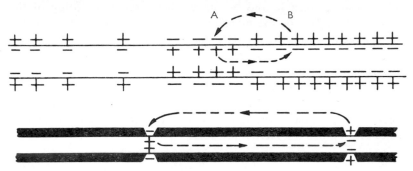

Fig. 12. Diagrams illustrating the local circuit theory; the upper sketch represents an unmyelinated nerve fibre, the lower a myelinated nerve fibre.

system could give only one impulse and would be useless for signalling information. The existence of a transient action potential and the possibility of sending trains of impulses is explained by the observations which show that the rise in sodium permeability is short-lived and that the potassium permeability increases during the latter part of the action potential. The effect of these changes is that after about 0·3 msec potassium ions leave the fibre faster than sodium ions enter. The outward migration of potassium ions restores the original potential difference across the membrane capacity and after a brief period the fibre is once more in a condition in which it can again conduct an impulse.

In most invertebrates the nerve fibres are uniform structures and the impulse appears to spread smoothly from one point to the next. Owing to the large electrical capacity of the surface membrane, about 1 μF per cm^2 of membrane, and the high resistance per unit length of a small cylinder of axoplasm this type of conduction is rapid only if the fibre is large.[1] In the myelinated fibres which form the bulk of our own nerves a more economical method of achieving a high velocity has been achieved. These fibres are coated over most of their length with a layer of myelin which acts as an insulator and greatly reduces the mean

1. The velocity increases with diameter because the resistance per unit length of the axis cylinder is proportional to (diameter)$^{-2}$ whereas the capacity of the surface per unit length is proportional to diameter. A dimensional argument indicates that velocity should be proportional to (diameter)$^{\frac{1}{2}}$ in unmyelinated fibres and to the first power in myelinated axons (Rushton, 1951; Hodgkin, 1954).

capacity per unit length. The excitable membrane is exposed at the nodes of Ranvier and current flows between nodes in the manner shown in Figure 12. Some current is wasted in charging up the myelin but since the myelin sheath is relatively thick its capacity is much less than that of an excitable membrane. The effect of a saltatory conduction, in which activity jumps from one node to the next, is that the impulse is conducted faster and with less expenditure of energy than in an unmyelinated fibre of comparable size. Some of the evidence for the mechanism will be given in Chapter IV.

EVIDENCE FOR THE MEMBRANE THEORY

Propagation by local circuits[1]

Before considering the nature of the permeability changes, it is worth spending a little time on some simple tests which demonstrate the essential validity of various aspects of the membrane theory. To begin with, there are a number of experiments which prove beyond any reasonable doubt that the impulse is propagated by the local electric circuits which spread in front of the active region. One way of testing this point is to see whether the velocity of conduction can be altered by varying the electrical resistance of the fluid outside the nerve fibre. Figure 13 illustrates such an experiment. A single fibre, in this case from the shore crab, *Carcinus maenas*, was mounted in such a way that the stretch of nerve fibre between the stimulating and recording electrodes could be immersed either in a large volume of sea water or in oil. When the fibre was raised into oil it remained surrounded by a thin film of saline so that the composition of the external fluid was unchanged throughout the experiment. However, when in oil the cross-sectional area and hence the conductance of the external conducting path was greatly reduced and so a lower conduction velocity was expected. This is borne out by the experimental results which show that raising the fibre into oil increased the time taken to conduct a fixed distance by about 30 per cent. Experiments of the same type carried out subsequently with giant axons from *Loligo* gave increases of about 100 per cent. In this case it was unnecessary to use oil and the external resistance could be changed by the simple operation of raising the fibre out of sea water into moist air. (Oil was used occasionally but had the same effect as air.) The change in velocity was larger in the squid axon because the resistance of the external conducting path was higher in proportion to that of the axon in a 500μ fibre than in a 30μ fibre.

1. It is convenient to distinguish between the local circuit theory, which deals only with the part played by electric currents in propagation, and the membrane theory which attempts to give a more complete picture of the whole chain of events.

The giant axon of *Loligo* was also used to determine whether the conduction velocity could be increased by metallic conductors. This was done by placing the stretch of fibre between the stimulating and recording leads on a grid of platinum strips (Fig. 14). These were sealed into a moist chamber and arranged so that they could be connected together

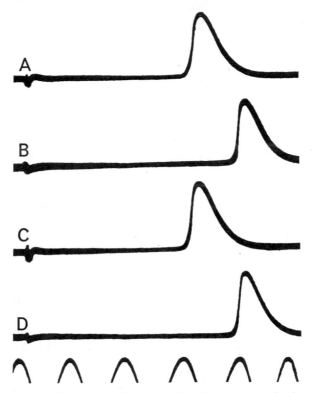

Fig. 13. Effect of changing external resistance on conduction velocity. A and C, action potential recorded with sea water covering 95% of conduction distance, B and D fibre completely immersed in oil. Conduction distance, 13 mm. Time, msec. Axon from *Carcinus maenas*, 30μ in diameter. (From Hodgkin, 1939.)

by means of a mercury switch. When the strips were connected the velocity increased about 16 per cent. The effect was not large but was striking to watch on the oscilloscope because it took place within the fraction of a second required to move the switch. Such an experiment affords strong evidence because the only agent known which could travel through a metallic short-circuit in the time available is an electric current. The reason why the increase in velocity was relatively small is that the electrodes were polarizable and made contact only at discrete points along one side of the nerve fibre.

On one occasion a giant axon afforded an opportunity for repeating an experiment carried out previously by Osterhout and Hill (1931) on

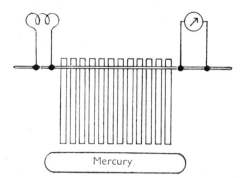

Fig. 14. Diagram of apparatus for short-circuiting fibre with metallic conductors. (From Hodgkin, 1939.)

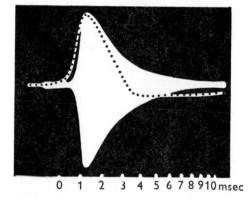

Fig. 15. Action potential (dotted curve) and increase in conductance (white band) in squid axon at about 6° C. (From Cole & Curtis, 1939.)

the exitable cells of the plant *Nitella*. A fibre which had been placed on the grid of metal strips developed a block between two of the strips. This was only effective when the strips were disconnected; if they were joined by the mercury contact, the action potential was able to traverse the injured region and so reach the recording electrodes.[1]

The increase in membrane conductance during the impulse

One of the best pieces of evidence for Bernstein's theory is that in all tissues so far examined the impulse is associated with a transient

1. For other evidence for the local circuit theory, see Auger, 1933; Hodgkin, 1937; Tasaki, 1939a, b, 1953; Katz & Schmitt, 1940, 1942; Huxley & Stämpfli, 1949a; del Castillo & Moore, 1959.

increase in the electrical conductivity of the membrane.[1] Figure 15 which is taken from the classical paper by Cole & Curtis (1939) demonstrates the increase in membrane conductance associated with the passage of an impulse past two electrodes placed on opposite sides of a giant axon from *Loligo*. The width of the white band is proportional to the increase in conductance; the dotted line gives the action potential. By analysing their results Cole & Curtis concluded that the resistance of the membrane fell from its resting value of 1000 ohm cm^2 to an active one of 25 ohm cm^2; neither the electrical capacity of the membrane nor the resistance of the axoplasm changed appreciably. As would be expected, the initial experimental rise of potential, which is due to the passive spread of current in front of the active region, preceded the rise in membrane conductance.

Development of potential differences at the membrane: perfusion of giant axons

If the action potential arises from permeability changes it should, in principle, be possible to replace the axoplasm inside the membrane by means of an aqueous solution of appropriate composition. The words 'in principle' must be added because a pessimist might suppose that removal of the axoplasm would be likely to destroy the membrane or at least to alter its physiological properties in a radical manner. Katz and I tried to perfuse axons in 1948 but met with little success – partly because the axoplasm is a firm gel and is not easily washed away. Recently P. F. Baker and T. I Shaw developed a method which has proved surprisingly successful.[2] One of the tricks that can be played with giant nerve fibres is to extrude axoplasm from the cut end. This is done by stroking with a glass rod or by running a device like a miniature garden roller over the fibre in a series of sweeps. In order to remove the axoplasm it is necessary to squeeze the fibre quite firmly and until recently everyone assumed that the surface membrane must be severely damaged during the extrusion. Baker and Shaw thought it would be a good idea to test this point. Their first type of experiment is illustrated by Figure 16 which was obtained at a later stage of the investigation. The action potential was recorded with external electrodes using the arrangement shown in the right-hand part of the figure. Record A shows the usual diphasic response in the right-hand half of an intact fibre. In B, the axoplasm from the right-hand half had been extruded; the

1. Blinks, 1936; Cole & Curtis, 1938, 1939; Katz, 1942; Fessard, 1946; Tasaki & Mizuguchi, 1949.
2. Baker & Shaw, 1961; Baker, Hodgkin & Shaw, 1961. For alternative methods of perfusion, see Oikawa, Spyropoulos, Tasaki & Teorell, 1961.

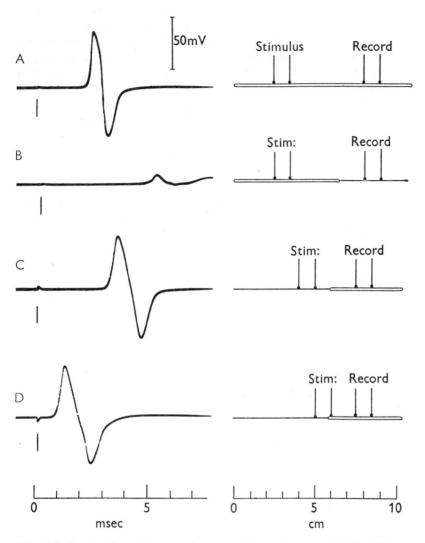

Fig. 16. Restoration of externally recorded action potential by filling 'sheath' with axoplasm. A, intact axon; B, right-hand half extruded; C, right-hand half filled by moving in axoplasm from left-hand half. D as in C but two hours later. (From Baker, Hodgkin & Shaw, 1961.)

action potential was still present, but owing to the increased internal resistance, it was propagated more slowly and the component recorded with external electrodes was greatly reduced. On moving axoplasm from the left-hand into the right-hand part, the external action potential was restored to its original amplitude (c) and was still the same size two hours later (D).

Experiments of this kind established that extrusion did not destroy the membrane and encouraged Baker & Shaw to try replacing axoplasm with an artificial solution. The method is to tie a cannula into one end of the fibre, squeeze out axoplasm from the other and then to reinflate the fibre with a solution such as potassium sulphate. In about 70 per cent of cases, reinflated axons conducted impulses and often continued to do so for several hours. After getting the method going, Baker & Shaw asked me to join them which I was naturally very happy to do. Our first task was to find out what types of perfusion fluid were capable of maintaining excitability. The solutions used in the early experiments contained magnesium and bicarbonate ions but it turned out that neither is necessary. The internal solution should be isotonic and must contain potassium rather than sodium but the nature of the anion is not important, for action potentials were obtained with isotonic solutions of potassium chloride, sulphate, methyl-sulphate and isethionate. The last substance was used because it is present at a high concentration in squid nerve. However, it does not seem to be playing any immediate part in the conduction of impulses because the action potential in axons filled with isethionate is much the same as in those filled with one of the other anions. All the solutions were calcium-free and were normally buffered to pH 7·5 with phosphate. A large volume, up to 150 times that of the fibre, could be perfused without making it inexcitable.

Experiments with internal electrodes showed that the electrical properties of fibres perfused with isotonic potassium solutions were not very different from those of intact axons. The action potential, 100–110 mV, and resting potential, 50–70 mV, were of the usual magnitude and as can be seen from Figure 17 the time course of the response of a perfused fibre (A) was similar to that of a normal fibre (B).

Evidence that the perfusion fluid had rapid access to the surface membrane was provided by the speed with which the action potential was blocked by replacing K with Na. Provided the sodium solutions were not applied for too long their effect was completely reversible and both block and restoration might occur in 10–20 seconds, the speed of the effect depending on the rate of flow and on the extent to which the dead space could be reduced.

38

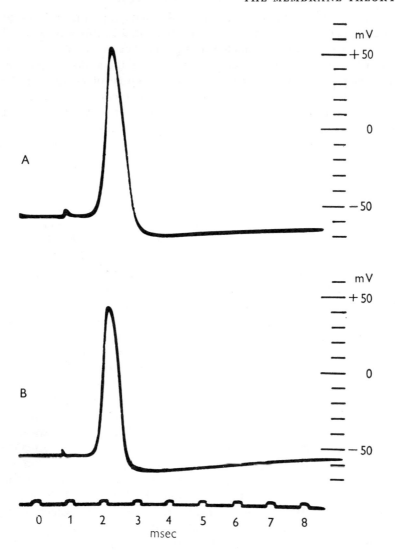

Fig. 17. A, action potential recorded with internal electrode from extruded axon filled with potassium sulphate (16° C); B, action potential of an intact axon, with same amplification and time scale (18° C). The voltage scale gives the potential of the internal electrode relative to its potential in the external solution—with no correction for junction potential. (From Baker, Hodgkin & Shaw, 1961.)

39

In spite of the fact that extrusion and subsequent perfusion removed about 95 per cent of the axoplasm, fibres treated in this way survived for several hours and conducted a large number of impulses, for instance 3×10^5. This would seem to fit well with the notion, implicit in the membrane theory, that the immediate source of energy for the conduction of impulses is provided by the ionic concentration gradients. If chemical reactions are concerned in the permeability changes it would seem that these must occur at sites, either in or near the membrane, from which enzyme and reactants cannot easily diffuse away.

Bernstein's suggestion about the origin of the resting potential is supported by the observation that the potential disappears if the external concentration of potassium is made equal to the internal concentration and that at high external potassium concentrations the potential agrees with the Nernst equation.[1] The failure of the equation at low external concentrations suggests that some ion besides K can also affect the potential. In muscle where the distribution of potassium and chloride ions approximates to a Donnan distribution[2] there is evidence that both K and Cl ions control the potential, the transport number for K being about 0·3 and for Cl about 0·6.[3] Some other explanation has to be sought in squid nerve for the tracer measurements of Caldwell & Keynes (1960) suggest a low chloride permeability. Our own measurements with perfused axons point in the same direction, for replacement of potassium sulphate with potassium chloride caused little change in resting potential. On the other hand since total replacement of KCl by NaCl reduced the resting potential to zero it would seem that there is no large e.m.f. in parallel with the potassium concentration cell and that Bernstein's hypothesis is substantially correct. Why then is the resting potential relatively insensitive to $[K]_o$ at concentrations below 20 mM?

In order to throw light on this somewhat puzzling situation we determined the relation between internal potassium concentration and resting potential using mixtures of isotonic KCl and NaCl. Figure 18 shows the result. With sodium chloride inside the fibre the potential was close to zero but it increased rapidly as K replaced Na; reaching a value of 40–50 mV at an internal potassium concentration of 150mM. A further rise from 150 to 600 mM increased the potential by only about 10 mV as against the 35 mV expected from the Nernst equation. In other words there is a kind of saturation phenomenon which prevents the resting potential rising about 50–60 mV. This is about the level at which the resting potential limits when the external potassium concentration is reduced. The effect almost certainly occurs because the potas-

1. Curtis & Cole, 1942, and other references on p. 27.
2. Boyle & Conway, 1941.   3. Hodgkin & Horowicz, 1959b.

sium permeability falls as the resting potential rises. If, as is probable, the membrane has some kind of indiscriminate leak to sodium ions, one would expect the limiting value of the resting potential to be fixed by the value at which the outward amount of potassium through the permeability channel just balances the inward leak of sodium. In sup-

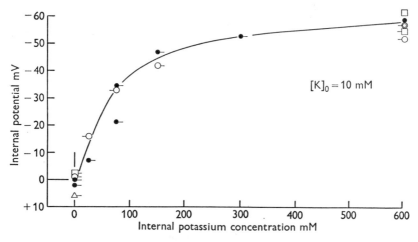

Fig. 18. Effect of internal potassium concentration on resting potential. External solution, sea water; internal solution, sodium chloride-potassium chloride solutions isotonic with sea water. (Baker, Hodgkin & Shaw, 1961.)

port of such an explanation Dr Shaw has shown that the curve in Figure 18 is in good agreement with that calculated from equations which allow for the variation of potassium permeability with membrane potential.

Although the perfusion method illustrates some of the complexities and difficulties which beset any one who tries to apply physical theories to biological membranes, it also permits a rather dramatic test of the idea that potassium ions control the resting potential. Suppose that the experiment starts with the axon surrounded by sea water (10 mM–K 450 mM–Na) and filled with 600 mM–KCl; the resting potential is then about 60 mV, inside negative. If the KCl inside the fibre is replaced by NaCl the potential falls to a value near zero. If now the potassium concentration in the external fluid is raised to 600 mM the normal situation is reversed and the inside of the fibre should become positive with respect to the outside. This is what happens; with isotonic KCl outside and isotonic NaCl inside, the interior of the fibre becomes 50–60 mV positive to the external solution.

If the action potential depends on an increase of sodium perme-

41

ability, increasing sodium inside the fibre should reduce the size of the spike and eventually make the fibre inexcitable. Figure 19 illustrates the effect of different concentrations of Na, the internal anion being sulphate. In the middle record, B, which was obtained first, one quarter of the potassium inside the fibre was replaced by sodium. On removing all

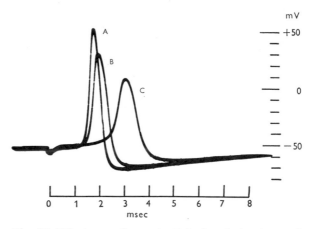

Fig. 19. Effect on action potential of replacing internal potassium with sodium ions. A, isotonic potassium sulphate; B, $\frac{1}{4}$ K replaced by Na. C, $\frac{1}{2}$ K replaced by Na. The records were obtained in the order B, A, C. (Baker, Hodgkin & Shaw, 1961.)

the sodium the action potential increased as can be seen in record A. The potential does not become infinite because the discrimination between K and Na is not perfect, the selectivity factor P_{Na}/P_K being probably of the order of 10. If half the potassium was replaced by sodium the action potential fell and was only slightly bigger than the resting potential. A further replacement of K by Na blocked conduction in a reversible manner. These results are a natural corollary to the well-known observations that a rise in external sodium increases the action potential and that a decrease reduces it (Fig. 20). The inference from both sets of experiments is that the difference in sodium concentration provides the electromotive force which generates the action potential.

Movements of ions during activity

One of the strongest pieces of evidence for the sodium and potassium form of the membrane theory is that conduction of impulses is associated with a substantial increase in the rate at which sodium and potassium ions move down their concentration gradients. The quantity of Na

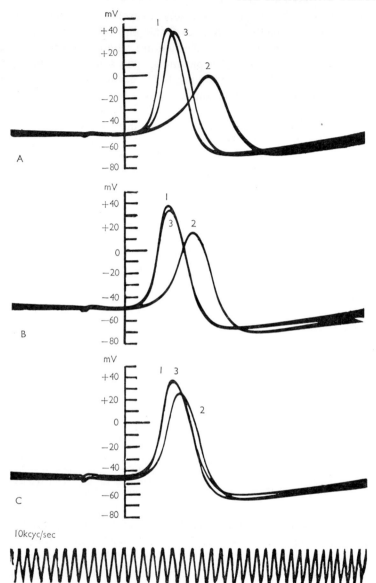

Fig. 20. Effect of sodium deficient external solutions on the action potential. Records labelled 1 and 3 were with the axon in sea water. a2 with $\frac{1}{3}$ sea water, $\frac{2}{3}$ isotonic dextrose; b2 with $\frac{1}{2}$ sea water, $\frac{1}{2}$ isotonic dextrose; c2 with 0·7 sea water, 0·3 isotonic dextrose. (From Hodgkin & Katz, 1949.)

43

which enters, or of K which leaves, can be determined with tracers or by sensitive analytical methods such as flame photometry or activation analysis. In expressing the results, which are summarised in Table 3, quantities are usually given in picomoles per square centimetre of membrane; 1 picomole (pmole) equals 10^{-12} gram ion, or $6·02 \times 10^{11}$ ions. When using tracers, it is important to observe the flow in both

Table 3. Net Movements of Na and K Associated with 1 Impulse
1 pmole $= 10^{-12}$ mole $= 6 \times 10^{11}$ ions

Preparation	Fibre Diameter μ	Temperature $°C$	Na Entry	K loss	CV/F
				pmole/cm²	
Carcinus axon	30	17	—	2	1·2
Sepia axon	200	15–20	3–4	3–4	1·2
Squid axon	500	20	3–4	3–4	1·2
Squid axon	500	6	—	9	1·2
Frog muscle fibre	100	20	15	10	6
				pmole/cm	
Frog myelinated nerve	10*	20	5×10^{-5}	$3–6 \times 10^{-5}$	$1·6 \times 10^{-5}$

* Root mean square of all myelinated axons in Figure 11 of Erlanger & Gasser, 1937.

For further details see Hodgkin, 1958; references are Asano & Hurlbut, 1958; Grundfest & Nachmansohn, 1950; Hodgkin & Horowicz, 1959a; Hodgkin & Huxley, 1947; Keynes, 1949, 1951a & b; Keynes & Lewis, 1951; Rothenberg, 1950; Shanes, 1951 & 1954, Weidmann, 1951.

In the right-hand column C is the membrane capacity per sq. cm. or in the last row the capacity per unit length, V is the amplitude of the action potential and F the Faraday. V is taken as 0·12 volts throughout, C as $1\mu F/cm^2$ for unmyelinated axons; $5\mu F/cm^2$ for muscle and 13 pF/cm for myelinated axons (see Table 4).

directions through the membrane. For example in the giant nerve fibres of cuttlefish (Keynes (1951b) found that each impulse was associated with an inflow of Na of $10·3$ pmole/cm², but there was also an outflow of Na of $6·6$ pmole/cm². The net entry was therefore taken as $3·7$ pmole/cm², a quantity in approximate agreement both with the potassium lost per impulse and with the movements deduced from the net gain of Na during a long period of stimulation.

An entry of 4 pmole Na through one square centimetre of surface is more than enough to account for the action potential. The quantity of charge required to change the voltage across a one-microfarad condenser by 120 mV is 0.12×10^{-6} coulomb. This is equivalent to 1.2×10^{-12} mole of monovalent cation which is only one-third of the observed entry of sodium. While it would have been disturbing if the entry of Na had been less than the theoretical minimum, there is no difficulty in accounting for one that is larger. In addition to charging the membrane capacity during the rising phase much of the Na entry is an immediate exchange with K, particularly during the early part of the falling phase when the permeability to both ions is high. A fall in temperature which increases the duration of the action potential should and does increase the quantity of ions crossing the membrane during an impulse (Shanes, 1954).

In Chapter v we shall consider an indirect method of calculating how much sodium should cross the membrane and will see that the quantity predicted is in fair agreement with that found experimentally.

Studies of single muscle fibres from frogs[1] indicate that these cells, which have an unusually large membrane capacity, also have larger ionic movements than nerve, the entry of sodium ions per impulse being about 15 and the loss of potassium about 10 pmole/cm^2. Even if the membrane capacity is as high as $5-10$ μF/cm^2,[2] and there is some doubt[3] whether such a large value is appropriate to the action potential, the quantities of Na and K crossing the surface are still more than enough to generate the electrical change.

The quantities of sodium and potassium ions which cross the surface of a myelinated axon in one impulse are much smaller than those in an unmyelinated axon of similar size. This is to be expected because the ionic currents are concentrated at the node and the electrical capacity of the myelin sheath is much less than that of a single cell membrane. However, as Shanes (1958) has pointed out the relation between the number of ions moving and the total capacity per unit length is similar to that in an unmyelinated axon. Asano and Hurlbut (1958) found that stimulating a frog's sciatic nerve at 50/sec for an hour caused a gain of sodium and a loss of potassium of about 5 μmole per gram wet weight.[4] According to an earlier calculation[5] there are 6×10^5 cm of myelinated axon in one gram of frog nerve and the mean capacity per unit length, which should be independent of diameter, is about 13 pF/cm. From this it follows that the quantity of Na which enters 1 cm length of fibre in one impulse is about 5×10^{-17} mole as against a theoretical mini-

1. Hodgkin & Horowicz, 1959a.   2. Fatt & Katz, 1951.
3. Fatt, 1961.   4. See Connelly, 1959.
5. Hodgkin, 1951. In myelinated axons the mean capacity per unit length is independent of diameter if node spacing and myelin thickness are proportional to diameter and the width of the nodal gap is constant.

mum of $1 \cdot 6 \times 10^{-17}$; the two quantities are therefore in about the same ratio as in giant axons.

It is interesting to compare the density of ionic movement in an unmyelinated axon and at a node. In an unmyelinated axon about 20,000 sodium ions cross 1 square micron of surface in one impulse. In a myelinated axon with 5 nodes per centimetre 6×10^6 sodium ions enter each node in one impulse. If the area of nodal membrane is taken as 20 square micra the number entering through unit area comes to 300,000 which fits with the observation that the ionic current densities are about ten times greater at the node than in giant axons. Presumably the sites at which ions cross the membrane are crowded together more closely at the node than they are in the membrane of an unmyelinated axon.

Substitutes for sodium

Although the action potential of excitable tissues is invariably accompanied by an increase in the conductivity of the membrane it does not always depend on an inward movement of sodium. In several tissues certain quarternary ammonium ions[1] can replace sodium and, as was first shown by Overton (1902), lithium is always an effective substitute. Such experiments show that cells which normally work with sodium can use substitutes but there are certain tissues in which the action potential is little influenced by the presence of absence of sodium. In crab muscle, under appropriate conditions, calcium or other divalent ions provide the inward current[2] and in the plant cell, *Chara*, Gaffey and Mullins (1958) consider that an exit of chloride from the concentrated sap is the primary process. However, in spite of these exceptions, the sodium-potassium mechanism is sufficiently widespread to justify the experimental effort devoted to it.

1. Lorente de Nó, 1949; Lüttgau, 1958.
2. Fatt & Katz, 1953; Fatt & Ginsborg, 1958.

CHAPTER IV

Saltatory conduction in myelinated nerve

In the previous lecture I mentioned some of the experiments which prove that conduction of impulses depends on the electric currents that spread in front of the active region. In unmyelinated nerve and in muscle the spread of current is continuous and conduction appears to be a uniform process. But in myelinated nerve, there is now much evidence for the theory, proposed by Lillie in 1925, that conduction is discontinuous or saltatory and that the impulse skips from one node to the next. On this view the active generation of current is confined to the nodes of Ranvier whereas the myelin acts as an insulator with a low electrical capacity which increases conduction velocity by making the local circuit act at a considerable distance ahead of the active region. In most excitable tissues the inward current, which enables the impulse to propagate without decrement is carried by sodium ions moving down their concentration gradient during the period of high sodium permeability. Applied to the saltatory theory this means that sodium ions enter myelinated axons only at the nodes but depolarize the whole fibre by local circuit action. No one has yet been able to test this particular point directly but there is now a large body of evidence in favour of the saltatory theory.

Experiments showing that excitation occurs at nodes of Ranvier

In his book on the microphysiology of nerve, published in 1934, Kato described experiments by Kubo and Ono, in which an electrical stimulus was applied at various points along a nerve fibre. It was found that the threshold was lowest when the cathode was opposite a node and highest near the middle of an internode. In this type of experiment a strong stimulus is still effective when the cathode is in the internode because current spreads along the fibre and stimulates an adjacent node. The current can be confined by using a tripolar arrangement in which a central cathode is placed between equipotential anodes. In that case, as was first shown by Tasaki, the electrical threshold is low if the cathodal region contains a node but is virtually infinite if it does not.[1] During the late 1930's Tasaki carried out an elegant analysis of the interaction

1. Tasaki, 1939a; Tasaki & Mizuguchi, 1948; Lussier & Rushton, 1952.

between pairs of electrical stimuli applied across neighbouring air gaps, and proved beyond any doubt that the stimulating current had its effect at the node. He also showed that the myelin sheath had an appreciable capacity and that its electrical resistance must be much greater than that of the nodal membrane.[1]

Experiments showing that nodes of Ranvier are especially sensitive to blocking agents

In 1936 Kato summarised evidence, obtained by Tasaki and others in his laboratory, which showed that agents like cocaine or urethane affected nodes but had no action on internodes. The experiments of Erlanger and Blair (1938) indicated that salt-free glucose solutions sometimes block at specific points spaced about 2 mm apart in the individual fibres of the frog. They had previously examined the effect of anodal polarization and had found that the action potential of a polarized fibre showed discrete steps and that segments of the action potential disappeared as units. This led them to suggest that anodal polarization blocks the nerve at specific points and that the action potential arose in a segmental manner.[2]

Experiments carried out since the last war have fully confirmed Kato's generalization and Stämpfli (1952) gave a long list of chemicals or agents, for example ultraviolet light, which affect nodes but not internodes. A striking example is that although cooling a whole fibre greatly prolongs the action potential, cooling an internode has no effect on the duration of the longitudinal current associated with the impulse.[3]

Evidence that the action potential arises at the nodes of Ranvier

In the saltatory theory it is assumed that the inward current which generates the rising phase of the action potential is confined to the nodes. This does not mean that the potential difference across the myelin remains unchanged or that a spike can only be recorded at the nodes. For each internode acts like a short segment of cable with distributed capacity and the potential difference across the sheath in the middle of the internode will rapidly approach the mean of the potential differences across the nodal membranes at either end of the cable. Since the conduction time between adjacent nodes is 5–10 per cent of the duration of the action potential it follows that the amplitude of the spike at the middle of an internode should be only slightly smaller than that at the nodes. On the other hand since the duration of the rising phase is comparable to the internodal conduction time one would

1. Tasaki, 1939a, b, 1953.   2. Erlanger & Blair, 1934.
3. Hodler, Stämpfli & Tasaki, 1951.

expect the rate of rise of the action potential to be less in the middle of the node. Both these points – constancy of amplitude and a substantial decrease in the rate of rise in the internode – were demonstrated directly by Hodler, Stämpfli & Tasaki (1952).

In order to prove the saltatory theory in a rigorous manner it is desirable to measure the radial current at different points along the

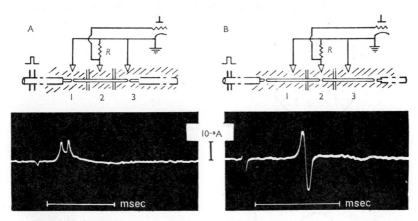

Fig. 21. A, membrane current through 1 mm long region of internode. B, similar to A but with a node in the central pool. Outward current upwards. (From Tasaki, 1959.)

fibre. The first tests of this kind were made by Tasaki & Takeuchi (1941 & 1942) and described by them in two papers published in Germany during the Second World War. After the war these articles were not available in many parts of the world and it was some time before the importance of Tasaki & Takeuchi's experiments was generally recognized. Figure 21, which is taken from Tasaki (1959), illustrates their method and the results which they obtained with it. A single fibre lay in three pools of Ringer's fluid separated by air gaps spaced about 1 mm apart. In one case, A, the pool contained only the myelinated part of the axon, in the other, B, it contained a node. The recording arrangement was designed to measure radial current and should do so exactly if the resistance R is low compared to the resistance across the air gaps. Suppose that a current i_{12} flows in the external circuit from pool 1 to pool 2 and a current i_{23} from pool 2 to pool 3 then the difference between these two currents, which is equal to the current entering the fibre in pool 2, is recorded across the resistance R.

It can be seen at once that records A and B are entirely different. In A the radial current is outward as would be expected if the myelinated parts of the fibre are discharging passively into the node – there are two peaks because the right-hand node discharges later than the left-hand one. In record B there is first a phase of outward current as the node is passively depolarized and then a phase of inward current when it is active. The absence of any corresponding phase of inward current in the left-hand record provides strong evidence that the inward current, on which propagation depends, is confined to the node of Ranvier.

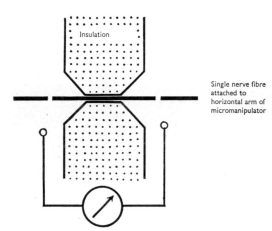

Fig. 22. Arrangement used by Huxley & Stämpfli, 1949a, for measuring longitudinal current during activity of single myelinated fibre.

Huxley & Stämpfli (1949a) confirmed and extended the observations of Tasaki & Takeuchi. In their method the distribution of current during an impulse was measured by drawing a single fibre through a short length of fine capillary filled with Ringer's fluid (Fig. 22). With this arrangement a record of the potential difference across the capillary gave the longitudinal current in the external fluid as a function of time. By sliding the fibre through the capillary and taking a number of re-cords the longitudinal current was found as a function of time and distance. The radial current through the myelin or node of Ranvier was obtained by differentiating the longitudinal current with respect to distance, and the potential difference across the surface by integrating with respect to distance.

Figure 23 shows how the radial current varies with distance along the fibre. As in Tasaki & Takeuchi's experiments the inward current during the rising phase is confined to the node and the myelinated segments show only a smaller, outward component.

The position in a myelinated fibre is well summarized by Figure 24 which Huxley & Stämpfli derived from the experiment just considered. It shows the membrane potential and membrane current at the node

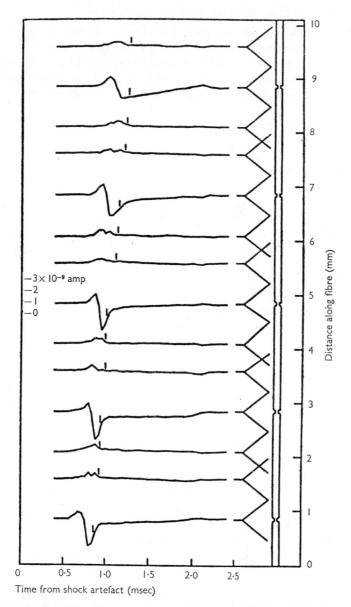

Fig. 23. Distribution and time course of membrane current in frog's myelin-ated nerve fibre. Each curve shows the difference between the longitudinal currents at two points 0·75 mm apart; the position of these two points relative to the nodes is indicated on the right. Vertical marks show the time of peak membrane potential. Outward current is plotted upwards. (From Huxley & Stämpfli, 1949a.)

and in the middle of the internode. The current through the myelin is of the kind expected in a system consisting of a capacity and resistance in parallel, that through the node can only be explained by postulating an active generation of current such as might occur if the nodal membrane underwent a large increase in the permeability to sodium.

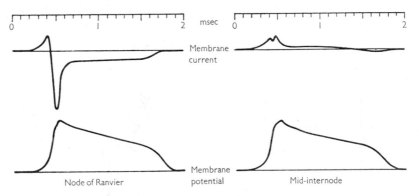

Fig. 24. Time course of membrane current and membrane potential at a node and in the middle of an internode. Outward current is plotted upwards. (From Huxley & Stämpfli, 1949b.)

Electrical characteristics of myelinated nerve fibres

By analysing the distribution of current and potential Huxley & Stämpfli (1949a) were able to calculate a number of constants of which one of the most important is the capacity of the myelin sheath. Their original estimates were uncertain in that they included an unknown factor α, the ratio of the specific resistance of the axoplasm to that of the surrounding medium. Subsequently they showed that α was about 1·2 and this value was used in calculating the constants in Table 4.

Several interesting conclusions can be drawn from the table. The dielectric constant of myelin appears reasonable for a structure composed of concentric layers of lipid with some protein and water between them. It is also clear that the myelin sheath is a good insulator since its specific resistance is about ten million times that of Ringer's fluid.

From the studies of the myelin sheath made by the methods of X-ray diffraction and electronmicroscopy it is known that lamellae corresponding to single Schwann cell membranes are spaced at a distance of 85Å. This means that there are about 240 lamellae in a sheath of thickness 2μ. Since the electrical capacity of the sheath is 0·0025–0·005 $\mu F/cm^2$ it follows that the capacity of each membrane is 0·6–1·2 $\mu F/cm^2$ which is close to the value of 1 $\mu F/cm^2$ found in many cell membranes.

Table 4. Electrical Characteristics of a Frog's Myelinated Fibre

Fibre diameter	14 μ
Thickness of myelin	2 μ
Distance between nodes (*l*)	2 mm
Area of nodal membrane (assumed)	22 μ^2
Resistance per unit length of axis cylinder (*r*)	140 megohm/cm
Specific resistance of axoplasm	110 ohm cm
Capacity per unit length of myelin sheath (*c*)	10–16* pF/cm
Capacity per unit area of myelin sheath	0·0025–0·005* μF/cm²
Dielectric constant of myelin sheath	5–10
Resistance x unit area of myelin sheath	0·1*–0·16 megohm cm²
Specific resistance of myelin sheath	500*–800 megohm cm
Capacity of node	0·6–1·5* pF
Capacity per unit area of nodal membrane	3–7* μF/cm²
Resistance of resting node	40–80 megohm
Resistance x unit area of nodal membrane	10–20 ohm cm²
Action potential	116 mV
Resting potential	71 mV
Peak inward current density	20 mA/cm²
Conduction velocity	23 m/sec
1/*lrc*	22*–36 m/sec

Data, mainly from Huxley & Stämpfli, 1949a, 1951a, collected by Stämpfli, 1952; with additional values, marked *, from Tasaki, 1955. To appreciate the physical significance of the final quantity, note that the time taken for potential to spread passively over a distance *l* in a cable with resistance *r* and capacity *c* is proportional to l^2rc; hence 1/*lrc* has the dimensions of a velocity.

The resistance of each lamella is about 500 ohm cm² which is of the same order as that in the membrane of a squid axon. The electrical evidence therefore fits rather well with the idea that the myelin sheath is composed of a large number of cell membranes piled on top of one another.

Values for the resistance and capacity of the nodal membrane are also given in Table 4. They are necessarily somewhat uncertain because of the difficulty of determining the area of membrane exposed at the node. If the width of the nodal gap is taken as 1μ, the capacity per unit area of the nodal membrane comes to 3–7 μF/cm² which is somewhat larger than that of most cell membranes. It is not clear whether the difference arises from an incorrect estimate of the nodal area or whether the membrane genuinely has a larger capacity per unit area. The membrane resistance, 10–20 ohm cm², is certainly much less than

53

that in a squid fibre and this is presumably connected with the ability of the node to give peak current densities about ten times greater than those in an unmyelinated axon.

Conduction velocity and the optimum thickness of myelin

The conduction velocity in a myelinated axon is determined partly by events at the node and partly by the time taken for local circuits to spread along the internode. It is clear that for a given external diameter there must be an optimum thickness of myelin at which the local circuits will spread most rapidly. If the myelin sheath is thin its capacity will be large; if it is thick the axis cylinder will be small and will have a high electrical resistance; in both cases the speed at which charge spreads must be less than at some intermediate thickness. As Rushton (1951) pointed out, the optimum ratio of internal to external diameter of the myelin sheath should be independent both of the fibre size and of the materials of which it is made. For a cable with a capacity per unit length c and a resistance per unit length r the constant which determines the spread of charge is $\frac{1}{rc}$; this has the dimensions of cm^2/sec and is analogous to a diffusion coefficient though many orders of magnitude greater. If the ratio of internal to external diameter of myelin is ρ and the external diameter is fixed, the longitudinal resistance of the axis cylinder is proportional to ρ^{-2} and the capacity to $\left(\ln\frac{1}{\rho}\right)^{-1}$. The spread of potential should therefore be most rapid when $\rho^2 \ln\frac{1}{\rho}$ is maximal. By the usual procedure for finding a maximum the optimal value of ρ is found to be $e^{-\frac{1}{2}} = 0.607$. This is appreciably less than the commonly accepted value of $\rho = 0.7$ for large myelinated axons. Allowance for leakage through the myelin does not alter the optimum but the argument is affected by the presence of a conducting pathway at the node. Thus if the nodal capacity were large, it would clearly pay to increase the internal diameter until the capacity of the myelin became comparable with that of the node. The argument can be made quantitative by calculating the value of ρ required to maximalize $\frac{1}{r\bar{c}}$ where $\bar{c}$ is the total capacity per unit length of nodes and internodes. According to Huxley & Stämpfli (1949b) the nodal capacity is $\frac{1}{3}$ of the internodal capacity whereas Tasaki (1955) found the fraction to be about 0·5.

54

If a ratio of 0·40 is assumed, $\dfrac{1}{r\bar{c}}$ is maximal when $\rho = 0.70$, a value in reasonable agreement with those of 0·69 (Gasser & Grundfest, 1939), 0·71 (Donaldson & Hoke, 1905) or 0·74 (Sanders, 1948).[1]

1. This is for the largest fibres; the lower values given for smaller fibres may be due to section thickness.

CHAPTER V

The nature of the permeability changes and calculation of the action potential

During the last fifteen years much quantitative information has been obtained by a method, often known as the voltage-clamp technique, in which the membrane potential is displaced to a new value and held there by electronic feedback. The current which flows through a definite area of membrane under the influence of the impressed voltage is measured with a separate amplifier. The early work was done on squid axons first by Cole[1] and later by Huxley, Katz and myself.[2] More recently Frankenhaeuser[3] has extended the analysis to the node of Ranvier; he finds certain differences from the giant axon but the broad picture is very much the same.

In explaining the point of the method it is convenient to refer to an electrical model of a nerve fibre. In Figure 25 the resistance labelled r represents the axis cylinder which connects different parts of the membrane together. Our conceptual nerve is supposed to be in a large volume so that the outside fluid is equipotential and can be replaced by a short-circuit. A single element of the membrane is shown and one must think of a large number of such elements connected together forming a continuous cable. The principal components of each element are the membrane capacity C, the potassium battery V_K, and resistance, R_K, and the sodium battery V_{Na} and resistance R_{Na}. The contribution of ions passing through channels which do not change during activity are represented by a leakage resistance, R_L, and a battery, V_L. However, the leakage current is small and can be disregarded in a preliminary description.

When an impulse propagates along a nerve fibre the internal potential changes with time and distance, and currents varying in time flow through all the elements in the cable. The voltage clamp technique simplifies the situation. First, all parts of the inside of the axon are

1. Cole, 1949. See also Marmont 1949, and recent papers by Cole's group in the *Journal of General Physiology* and the *Biophysical Journal*.
2. Hodgkin, Huxley & Katz, 1952.
3. Dodge & Frankenhaeuser, 1958 & 9; Frankenhaeuser, 1959 & 60.

connected together by a metal wire so that there are, at any rate in principle, no complications from current spreading along the fibre. In effect, instead of having to deal with a cable, the nerve can be treated as an isolated patch of membrane. The second simplification is that the experimenter controls the voltage across the membrane and so can

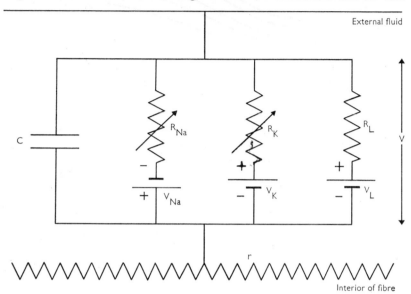

Fig. 25. Diagram of an element of the excitable membrane of a nerve fibre.

make it do what he wants. With suitable apparatus he can, for example, suddenly reduce the membrane potential to zero, a procedure equivalent to short-circuiting the membrane. If this is done the condenser discharges at once and thereafter only the ions flowing through R_{Na} and R_K contribute to the current. If the membrane is suddenly depolarized to some value between 20 and 110 mV the total ionic current (that is the current flowing after the almost instantaneous discharge of the condenser) consists of two phases. To begin with, sodium ions move down their concentration gradient, giving an inward current. However, this component is transient and after about a millisecond (at 10° C) it is replaced by an outward potassium current.[1] If the membrane is depolarized so that the total potential difference is equal to that of the sodium concentration cell, V_{Na}, there is no sodium current and only the delayed potassium current is seen. For displacements beyond V_{Na} the sodium current is outwardly directed (Fig. 26). The two components of the current vary with the concentrations of Na and K and by chang-

1. Hodgkin & Huxley, 1952a, 1953.

57

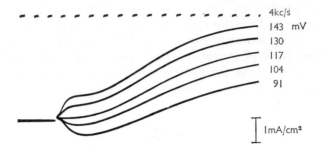

Fig. 26.—Membrane currents for different displacements of the membrane potential at a temperature of 3·5° C; outward current upwards. The figures at the right give the change in internal potential. (Hodgkin, Huxley & Katz, 1952.)

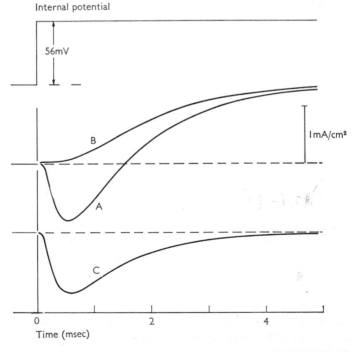

Fig. 27. Separation of membrane current into components carried by Na and K; outward current upwards. A, Current with axon in sea water $= I_{Na} + I_K$. B, Current most with of external Na replaced by choline $= I_K$. C, Difference between A and B $= I_{Na}$. Temperature 8·5° C. (From Hodgkin & Huxley, 1952a.)

Internal potential

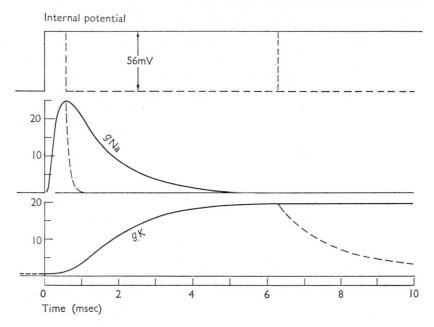

Fig. 28. Time course of sodium conductance (g_{Na}) and potassium conductance (g_{Na}) associated with depolarization of 56m V; vertical scale in mmho/cm². The continuous curves, which were derived from those in Figure 27, are for a maintained depolarization; broken curves give the effect of repolarizing the membrane after 0·6 or 6·3 msec. (From Hodgkin, 1958, based on Hodgkin & Huxley, 1952a & b.)

ing these concentrations the ionic current can be separated into its two components (Fig. 27). From the individual currents it is not difficult to estimate the conductivity of the membrane to each ion. Figure 28 illustrates the changes in conductance that occur when the potential of the inside of the fibre, initially negative to the external solution by 50–60 mV, is suddenly made positive by 56 mV, a change corresponding to suddenly short-circuiting the membrane. The sodium conductance starts at an exceedingly low value and rises rapidly to about 25 mmho/cm²; it then declines exponentially. The potassium conductance starts at a small but finite value; it does not change at once but rises in an S-shaped curve to a steady level. Both changes are graded and reversible; if the membrane potential is restored to its resting level the conductance reverts exponentially to its previous low value. The speed with which the conductance declines is about ten times greater for sodium than for potassium.

59

It is important to notice that the sodium conductance may be reduced in two different ways. If, as in the case shown by the dotted line in Figure 28, the resting potential is restored after a short time, the system controlling sodium permeability reverts rapidly to its resting state. In this kind of experiment a second pulse, applied immediately after the first, leads to a second rise in sodium conductance. On the other hand if the depolarization is maintained, the sodium conductance is reduced more slowly by a process known as inactivation.[1] After the sodium channel has been inactivated the membrane must be repolarized for a few milliseconds before a second pulse is again effective. The system controlling potassium permeability in squid nerve does not show any appreciable inactivation and the potassium conductance remains at a high level as long as the nerve is depolarized.

The sodium conductance, g_{Na}, is defined by the relation

$$I_{Na} = g_{Na} (V - V_{Na}) \tag{3}$$

where I_{Na} is the component of current carried by sodium ions, V is the membrane potential and V_{Na} the equilibrium potential for sodium, at which there is no tendency for Na^+ to move in either direction through the membrane (see equation 2, p. 31). A similar relation applies to the potassium conductance. Equation 3 is essentially a definition of g_{Na} and would be valid whatever the relation between I_{Na} and $V - V_{Na}$. However, its usefulness is greatly increased by the observation that with squid fibres in a normal ionic medium, the instantaneous value of the sodium current is directly proportional to the driving force $V - V_{Na}$. It is essential to include the word instantaneous in the statement because the conductance moves towards a new value when the potential is altered and the current is only proportional to voltage if the time interval between the two measurements of g_{Na} is made vanishingly small. At the node of Ranvier, Dodge and Frankenhaeuser (1959) found that the instantaneous relation between sodium current and voltage is non-linear and that it is best to work with a permeability defined by the constant field equation

$$I_{Na} = P_{Na} F \psi \frac{[Na]_i e^\psi - [Na]_o}{e^\psi - 1} \tag{4}$$

where ψ is VF/RT and R, T and F have their usual significance (p. 30).

Figure 29 shows a family of curves which define the changes in conductance associated with voltage steps of different amplitude. Although there is considerable variation in the magnitude and time course of the permeability change there is no sudden break or discontinuity. In the region of the electrical threshold, 10–30 mV, the conductance increases

1. Hodgkin & Huxley, 1952c.

Sodium conductance   Potassium conductance

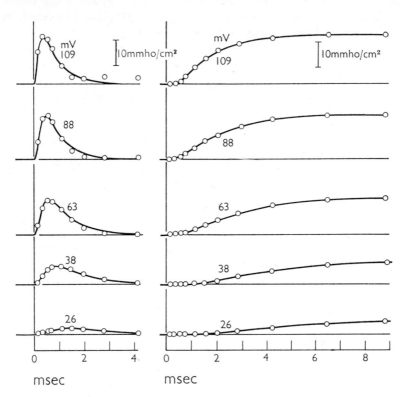

Fig. 29. Time course of sodium and potassium conductance for different displacements of membrane potential at 60° C; the numbers give the depolarization used. The circles are experimental estimates and the smooth curves are solutions of equations given in the Appendix. (From Hodgkin & Huxley, 1952d.)

very steeply, an e fold increase in conductance being caused by 4–6 mV more depolarization.

The circles in Figure 29 are from experimental measurements and the smooth curves have been drawn from a quantitative theory which Huxley and I developed. The equations underlying the curves can be given a physical meaning but our main object in developing the subject theoretically was to obtain empirical relations which described the changes in permeability.

Fitting theoretical equations to biological processes is often not a very profitable business, but in this case Huxley and I had a particular

61

reason for carrying out such an analysis. Nerve fibres undergo all sorts of complicated electrical changes under different experimental conditions and it is not at all obvious that they can be explained by relatively simple permeability changes of the kind seen in Figure 29.

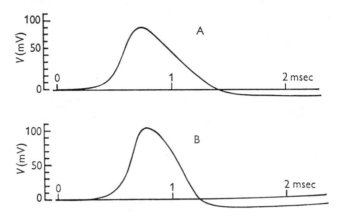

Fig. 30. Propagated action potentials in A, theoretical model, and B, squid axon at 18·5° C. The calculated velocity was 18·8 m/sec and the experimental velocity 21·2 m/sec. (From Hodgkin & Huxley, 1952d.)

The shape of the propagated action potential

To begin with, let us consider the most interesting case of an action potential propagating steadily along a uniform length of axon. The mathematical question asked can be put like this. Consider a membrane which undergoes changes in permeability of the kind shown in Figure 29: make it into a long tube, fill it with potassium ions inside and put sodium ions outside. We then ask whether such a model will give an action potential of the correct form and whether the velocity of propagation will be the same as that found experimentally. As can be imagined this is an awkward theoretical problem and the equations have to be solved numerically, or with a computer. However, the result is highly satisfactory because, as can be seen from Figure 30, the numerical solution obtained by Huxley agrees well with the experimentally determined action potential. There is also good agreement between the calculated and observed values of the conduction velocity.

Having carried out such an analysis it is possible to give a more quantitative picture of the sequence of events during the impulse. Figure 31 shows the calculated variation of sodium and potassium conductance during the theoretical action potential. As the impulse advances, the potential difference across the membrane just ahead of the active region is altered by electric currents flowing in a local circuit through the axoplasm and external fluid; this causes a rise in the con-

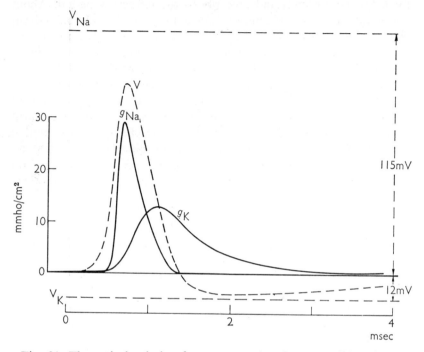

Fig. 31. Theoretical solution for propagated action potential and conductances at 18·5° C. (From Hodgkin & Huxley, 1952d.) Total entry of sodium = 4·33 pmole/cm²; total exit of potassium = 4·26 pmole/cm².

ductance to sodium ions, which enter the fibre making the inside positive and giving the current required to activate the next section of nerve. At the crest of the impulse the slower changes which result from depolarization begin to take effect. The sodium conductance declines and the potassium conductance rises so that the rate at which potassium ions leave the fibre exceeds the rate at which sodium ions enter; this makes the potential swing towards the equilibrium potential of the potassium ion. As the potential approaches the resting level any sodium conductance which has not been inactivated is cut off; so that the rate of repolarization may be accelerated. This last effect is conspicuous in myelinated fibres and although it is not obvious in a squid fibre at 18° c, at 6° c both the experimental and theoretical action potentials

63

show it quite plainly. (Temperature has a large effect on the rate at which the permeabilities change and in this way alters the form of the action potential.) The slow effects of depolarization, raised potassium conductance and inactivation of the sodium carrying system, persist for a few milliseconds and give rise to the refractory period. About 5 msec after the spike, the fibre is back in its original condition and can conduct another impulse of the same form as the first. The only difference is that it has gained a small amount of sodium and lost a similar amount of potassium ions. These quantities can be calculated theoretically and are in good agreement with those found experimentally.

The number of Na or K ions which cross the membrane during an impulse is small compared with the number inside a giant fibre and it takes many impulses to make an appreciable change in the internal concentration. However, the fibre must obviously pay the debt incurred and it does this at leisure during the period which follows a burst of electrical activity. Experiments dealing with this aspect are considered in Chapter VI.

Initiation of the action potential by electric currents

One of the conclusions from the voltage clamp experiments is that the sodium conductance increases smoothly as the membrane is depolarized and that there is no sudden break or discontinuity. This being the case, it is natural to ask why there should be a sharp threshold, or why the action potential should be all-or-nothing. The answer is that the sodium permeability and membrane potential are linked regeneratively in the following manner.

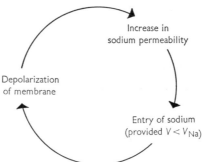

Increase in
sodium permeability

Depolarization
of membrane

Entry of sodium
(provided $V < V_{Na}$)

This means that when the membrane potential has been depolarized beyond a certain critical potential sodium ions enter the fibre at an accelerating rate and the potential moves rapidly towards the equilibrium potential of the sodium ion. On this basis, the threshold is the potential at which the inward sodium current just balances the outward potassium current. For subthreshold depolarizations, the outward potassium current exceeds the inward sodium current and the membrane repolarizes to its resting value. At the critical potential the sodium and potassium currents are equal and opposite and the potential can linger for some time in a state of unstable equilibrium before turning upwards into an action potential or downwards to the resting level.

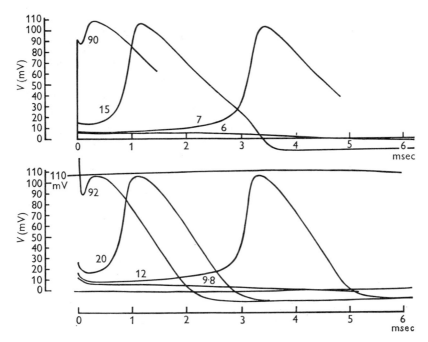

Fig. 32. Upper curves, theoretical solution for different initial depolarizations of a uniform area of membrane. Lower curves, tracings of membrane action potential at 6° C obtained on the same axon as that which gave Figure 29. The numbers attached to the curves give the strength of the shock in mμ coulomb/cm². (From Hodgkin & Huxley, 1952d.)

The lower part of Figure 32 illustrates what happens in an actual nerve following the displacement of the potential by a short shock. The upper curves were calculated by Huxley from the equations that we developed to describe the changes in permeability to Na and K.

Theoretical solutions corresponding to the application of a constant current, which have been calculated by Cole and his colleagues,[1] predict that, over a certain range of strengths, the membrane should

1. Cole et al., 1955; Fitzhugh, 1961.

give trains of impulses not unlike those often seen in the squid axon.[1] Other aspects of electrical activity for which the equations provide a satisfactory theoretical basis are the refractory period, subthreshold oscillations, anode break excitation[2] and the effects of temperature on the action potential.[3]

Accommodation to electrical stimuli

Although the question has not been examined critically, changes in permeability of the kind described here can probably account for the failure of a slowly rising current to set up an action potential. The rapid effect of depolarization is to increase sodium permeability; the slow effects are to inactivate the sodium-carrying system and to raise the potassium permeability. If the depolarization is gradual the slow effects predominate and block the regenerative action of the increase in sodium permeability. When tested with a slowly rising current, most nerves therefore pass into a refractory state without ever giving an action potential. The formal argument is that in squid and frog axons, though not in some crustacean axons, the slope conductance of the membrane in the steady state is positive for all values of membrane potential; hence all potentials are stable if approached sufficiently slowly.

Repetitive responses in crab nerve

Crustacean axons differ from the giant axons of *Loligo* in that constant currents set up long trains of impulses with frequencies as low as 5/sec (Fessard, 1936; Arvanitaki, 1938). An example from an experiment with a *Carcinus* axon is given in Figure 33 and shows that a 4·5 fold increase in current raises the frequency from 5/sec to 90/sec. This type of response is interesting because it may be what is required to account for the trains of impulses set up when sensory endings are depolarized by light or heat or by a mechanical or chemical stimulus. It is not explained by the permeability equations in the form developed for the squid axon, but it seems likely that relatively minor modifications to some of the parameters would give a model appropriate to crustacean axons and perhaps to certain sensory endings. However, without further experiments the interest attached to such calculations would be rather

1. An important difference is that the model predicts a train of indefinite duration whereas squid nerve often gives only a short train: see Fitzhugh, 1961, and Hagiwara & Oomura, 1958.
2. Hodgkin & Huxley, 1952d.
3. Huxley, 1959.

small since they would make no contribution to the much more fundamental problem of finding out how a stimulus depolarizes a nerve ending in the first place.[1]

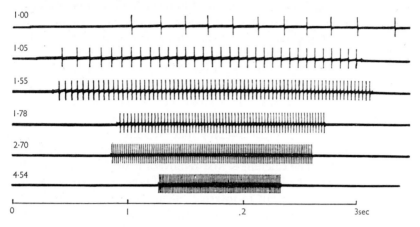

Fig. 33. Repetitive responses in single nerve fibre from *Carcinus maenas*. Electrical changes at the cathode produced by application of constant currents with strengths shown relative to the rheobase. The beginning and end of the applied current is marked by the slight artifact. (From Hodgkin, 1948.)

Nature of the permeability changes

Although little is known about the molecular organization of the membrane there are certain clues as to the type of mechanism which might be involved in the permeability changes. The dependence of permeability on membrane potential suggests that the changes might arise from movements of charged particles or dipoles. Such movements might have a direct effect on the ease with which ions cross the membrane or they might control chemical reactions which culminate in permeability changes. An interesting point about the system controlling permeability is the steepness of the relation between conductance and membrane potential – an e-fold increase of sodium conductance being brought about by a change of 5 mV or less in the potential difference across the membrane. In processes involving a single electronic charge, an e-fold change would be expected to occur in 25 mV and the much sharper characteristic of the nerve membrane suggests that the particles which control its permeability are multiply charged, or that several singly charged particles are involved at each site. The equations used

1. For an account of the generator potentials of nerve endings see Granit, 1955; Gray, 1959; Miller, Ratliff & Hartline, 1961.

67

by Huxley and myself, which are outlined in the Appendix, are a compromise between the ideas of several single-charged particles and a single, multiply charged particle. Thus the assumption that the potassium conductance is proportional to n^4 implies that the potassium gate is not open unless 4 particles are present in a certain region of the membrane, and the relation between n and membrane potential is roughly consistent with the individual particles being divalent.

It has been known for a long time that nerves fire spontaneously when the concentration of calcium is reduced and this has led to the suggestion that the increase in sodium permeability occurs because depolarization removes calcium ions from sites or carriers in the membrane.[1] Thus one might imagine that Na^+ crossed the membrane through special holes which are blocked when occupied by calcium but open to sodium when calcium is first removed. If the sites occupied by calcium were near the inner edge of the membrane and were accessible to external calcium but not to internal calcium the proportion of time for which the holes are open should be greatly increased either by reducing external calcium or by making the inside of the fibre less negative. In order to explain the steepness of the relation between membrane potential and sodium conductance it is necessary to suppose that several calcium ions are present in each hole and that all must be removed before the gate is open. This would not be inconsistent with the theory developed by Huxley and myself because the equations for the removal of a positively charged blocking particle are similar to those for the addition of a negatively charged activating particle. However, in following up the idea experimentally, Frankenhaeuser and I came across a difficulty which is less easily removed.[2] As might be expected from the theory we found that the effects of raising calcium or increasing the resting potential were roughly equivalent. However, the theory predicted that an e-fold increase of calcium concentration should be equivalent to an electrical change of at least 12·5 mV whereas our experiments gave a factor of 9 mV for an e-fold increase. The discrepancy might be explained by supposing that several calcium ions form a complex with an organic anion and that the sodium hole is plugged by this charged complex – but this makes the idea too speculative to be worth pursuing theoretically. A less dramatic way of accounting for the effects of calcium is to suppose that these ions are adsorbed on the outside of the membrane and that this alters the electric field in the membrane without changing the overall potential difference between external and internal solutions. In this case, calcium ions would be

1. Gordon & Welsh, 1948.
2. Frankenhaeuser & Hodgkin, 1957.

important in so far as their concentrations influenced the permeability and excitability of the membrane, but they could not be regarded as taking any direct part in the conduction of impulses.

There is now a large body of evidence for the view that acetylcholine is concerned in the transmission of impulses across certain synapses and junctions, for example in sympathetic ganglia, at parasympathetic nerve endings or at the junction between a voluntary nerve and a striated muscle. At other junctions, other substances such as adrenaline or noradrenaline act as the transmitting agent. The sequence of events at a neuromuscular junction is a release of acetylcholine by the nerve impulse from the nerve ending, diffusion of acetylcholine across a minute gap, and an action on the muscle membrane involving an unselective increase in the permeability to cations: this depolarizes the membrane of the muscle fibre and sets off a propagated action potential; the duration of the end-plate potential is kept short by an enzyme, cholinesterase, which hydrolyses the acetylcholine. Experiments by Katz and his colleagues have established two important differences between the increase of permeability produced by acetylcholine at the end-plate and that occurring in the rest of a nerve or muscle. The first is that the membrane becomes unselectively permeable to sodium and potassium with the result that the end-plate potential does not exceed the resting potential; the second is that the increase in permeability produced by the release of acteycholine is unaffected by membrane potential and is not electrically regenerative.[1]

Acetylcholine and the enzymes for its hydrolysis or synthesis are found in varying amounts in many tissues and Nachmansohn[2] has developed a unitary theory in which a release of acetylcholine is concerned with permeability changes in nerve and muscle as well as at the end-plate. He supposes that depolarization releases acetylcholine from its combination with one protein and that the free ester reacts with a second, receptor protein thereby causing an increase in sodium permeability; enzymatic hydrolysis of actylcholine permits the receptor protein to return to its resting condition and is responsible for repolarization and for inactivation of sodium permeability. One of the main pieces of evidence is that high concentrations of anticholinesterases block nerve impulses.

Since we do not know how the permeability changes occur it is difficult to be sure that acetylcholine is not concerned somewhere in the chain of events underlying the action potential. But the evidence is at best no more than suggestive and to my mind does not stand up to

1. See del Castillo & Katz, 1956; Grundfest, 1957.
2. See Nachmansohn, 1959.

the critical arguments which Katz and others have deployed.[1] To take only one example. The straightforward prediction from Nachmansohn's theory is that anticholinesterases should affect nerves in the same kind of way that they effect end-plates. That is to say, the period of increased sodium permeability should be greatly prolonged and repolarization should become very slow; block might or might not follow as a secondary consequence. The effects of anticholinesterases on nerve do not seem to be at all like this, for the action potentials of a partially blocked nerve are of the kind usually associated with some indiscriminate, mildly toxic action and are not greatly prolonged as the theory would seem to predict.

In thinking about the physical basis of the action potential perhaps the most important thing to do at the present moment is to consider whether there are any unexplained observations which have been neglected in an attempt to make the experiments fit into a tidy pattern. Difficulties of various kinds will no doubt occur to different people but perhaps the most puzzling observation is one made by A. V. Hill and his collaborators Abbott and Howarth (1958). Many years ago Hill showed that the initial heat in nerve was very small and that most of the heat liberation took place in a prolonged phase of recovery.[2] On reinvestigating the initial heat of crab nerve with better time resolution, Hill and his colleagues found that it was diphasic and that an initial phase of heat liberation was followed by one of heat absorption. The absolute magnitude of the cooling is about what would be expected from the recharging of the membrane capacity by an outward movement of potassium ions. However, the cooling seems to occur later than would be expected on this basis and Hill considers the idea untenable. An equally disturbing situation is found in the electric organ which cools when the organ discharges on open-circuit.[3] Bernstein predicted that the electric organ should cool if allowed to discharge into an external resistance[4] but a net cooling on open-circuit was totally unexpected and has so far received no satisfactory explanation.

1. del Castillo & Katz, 1956; Katz, 1960.　　2. Hill, 1932a.
3. Aubert, Fessard & Keynes, 1961; Aubert & Keynes, 1961.
4. Bernstein & Tschermak, 1906.

CHAPTER VI

The link between metabolism and ionic movements

The immediate effect of the passage of a train of impulses is that a nerve fibre gains a small quantity of sodium and loses a similar quantity of potassium ions. In giant axons, the changes in concentration resulting from a single impulse are very small, as can be seen by calculating that an outward movement of 4 pmole of K^+ through one square centimeter of membrane corresponds to a loss of only one-millionth of the total potassium in an axon with a diameter of 500μ. Such a fibre could conduct a large number of impulses, perhaps 5×10^5, without having to re-charge its batteries by metabolism. If the quantity crossing unit area is the same in all fibres, the change in concentration would be inversely proportional to diameter and in one impulse an 0.5μ fibre should lose one-thousandth instead of one-millionth of its internal potassium. This may explain why small fibres are more easily fatigued than large ones. But whether large or small, nerve fibres would be of no value to the animal unless they could use metabolic energy to drive sodium and potassium ions against concentration gradients. The necessity for such a system was foreseen by Overton (1902) who pointed out that human heart muscle carried out some 2.4×10^9 contractions in 70 years, yet, so far as he knew, contained as much potassium and as little sodium in old age as in early youth. Forty years later this idea was developed by Dean (1941) who showed theoretically that the distribution of potassium and chloride in muscle might be a passive consequence of an active extrusion of sodium but that active transport of either potassium or chloride ions would by themselves be inadequate. The reasoning is that an outwardly directed sodium pump would make the inside of the cell electrically negative with respect to the outside, so drawing in K^+ and expelling Cl^-. On the other hand an inwardly directed potassium pump would make the inside of the cell electrically positive, which would tend to draw in Cl^-. And an outwardly directed chloride pump which would also make the inside positive would tend to keep out K^+. The first alternative agrees with the electrical and chemical evidence; the second and third do not. Clearly all three ions might be affected to a greater or less degree by metabolic transport but the ion which must be moved is sodium. This follows directly from the fact that the resting

71

potential in muscle and nerve is fairly close to the equilibrium potential of potassium or chloride ions but is about 120–150 mV away from the equilibrium potential of the sodium ion. The situation is different in human red cells, which have a high internal chloride and in which there is clear evidence for an active uptake of potassium as well for an active output of sodium. Some consequences of a system in which there is a linkage, either complete or partial, between uptake of potassium and output of sodium, will be considered later.

In the years since Dean's paper was published much evidence has accumulated to show that nerve and muscle fibres, like many other cells, contain a secretory mechanism which uses metabolic energy to pump out sodium and to reabsorb potassium ions.[1] In skeletal muscle[2] and in mammalian red cells[3] this mechanism can be driven by glycolysis; in avian red cells[4] and probably in nerve it depends on oxidative metabolism.[5]

The recovery process is relatively slow and in large fibres it may take several hours to wipe out the effect of a burst of electrical activity. In the living animal, nerves are presumably in a steady state in which the intermittent entry of sodium associated with the conduction of impulses is balanced by the continuous activity of the system which extrudes sodium. The extra metabolism after activity might depend on an augmentation of the normal biochemical reactions, or new reactions might be brought in by the changes in membrane potential or ionic concentration which result from the passage of impulses. However, it is well to keep in mind a point raised by A. V. Hill (1932a) 'A resting nerve at 20° c gives out by oxidation about $6 \cdot 4 \times 10^{-5}$ cal per gm per second (Beresina, 1932): stimulated continuously at a maximum rate its heat production is about double (Hill, 1932b). Thus doing nothing at all, merely existing in a state of readiness to respond, it is using about half as much energy as when giving its greatest response.' The position is even more extreme in the giant axon of the squid, where Connelly & Cranefield (1953) found that continuous stimulation at 200/sec raised the resting oxygen consumption of 70 mm^3/g. hr by about 10 per cent. The small effect of stimulation seems to be associated with the large size of the fibre, rather than with the type of animal. For the same authors found that the small fibres of *Loligo*, which are much more subject to fatigue than the giant axon, increased their oxygen consumption by 50 per cent when stimulated at 2–5 impulses per second. It is not hard to see why there might be no very definite recovery metabolism in the giant axon. In the first place, as Hill pointed out in the sentences

1. See Ussing, 1959.   2. Frazier & Keynes, 1959.   3. Maizels, 1951.
   4. Maizels, 1954.   5. Shanes & Berman, 1955; Connelly, 1959.

which follow those just quoted, cells must expend energy continuously in order to balance the dissipation of concentration differences by unwanted leakage. To be more specific, sodium ions must leak into the fibre all the time, though perhaps at a very low rate, and continuous expenditure of energy is needed to keep the internal sodium concentration at a low level. Isolated axons may be in an abnormally leaky state but it seems rather unlikely that the inward leak of sodium *in vivo* would be less than one-tenth of the sodium influx measured with radioactive tracers *in vitro* – about 60 pmole/cm^2sec.[1] In order to compare this entry with that resulting from the natural traffic of impulses we must remember that when cruising at low speed a squid relies on an undulatory motion of its fins and that this does not involve the system of giant axons; respiratory movements which are mediated by radial muscle fibres are also not activated by these axons.[2] Jet propulsion which is used intermittently, as a means of escape or for capturing prey, does involve the giant axons and according to Thies (1957) the natural signal to the muscles which expels the jet is a group of 1 to 8 impulses in each axon. Since the frequency of the jets is 1/sec or less and since jet propulsion is reserved for emergencies, the mean frequency in life is unlikely to be more than a few impulses per minute; only about one ten thousandth of the maximum frequency which the fibre can transmit for short periods. The sodium entry associated with 3 impulses per minute at 18° c is 0·2 pmole/cm^2 sec; since this is 1/300 of the inward leak of sodium there would seem to be little evolutionary pressure for squids to develop a special recovery mechanism in their giant axons. The situation might be different in other nerves and Brink *et al.* (1952) give reasons for thinking that there may be a separate recovery system in frog nerve.

The action of metabolic inhibitors on ionic movements

Although there may be no clear-cut distinction between recovery and maintenance in giant axons they have many advantages in studying the link between metabolism and the uphill movements of ions. Figure 34 illustrates a rather simple type of experiment, carried out on a large fibre from the cuttlefish. The fibre was first loaded with an isotope of sodium, ^{24}Na, by stimulating it in a radioactive solution. (In squid axons radioactive solutions containing ^{22}Na are now usually injected for this type of experiment.) It was then washed with saline containing inactive sodium and samples of the fluid which flowed past the fibre were collected and counted at intervals. Since the labelled sodium ions inside the fibre became progressively diluted, the rate at which they left

1. Shanes & Berman, 1955. 2. Young, 1938.

the fibre decreased exponentially. This exponential decline appears as a straight line in Figure 34 because the ordinate has been plotted on a logarithmic scale. When enough counts of the normal outflow of ^{24}Na had been obtained, the sea water outside the fibre was replaced by a similar solution containing 0·2 mM – dinitrophenol. After an initial delay of about 10 minutes the efflux began to decline rapidly and fell in an hour to about one-twentieth of its previous value. This effect was largely reversed by washing the inhibitor away as can be seen from the

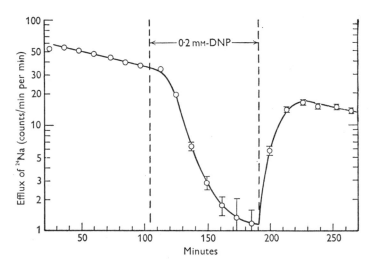

Fig. 34. Sodium efflux from a *Sepia* axon during treatment with dinitrophenol. At the beginning and end of the experiment the axon was in artificial water. Abscissa: time after end of stimulation in ^{24}Na sea water. Ordinate: rate at which ^{24}Na leaves axon. Vertical lines are $\pm$ 2 × S.E. Temperature 18° C. (From Hodgkin & Keynes, 1955a.)

recovery at the end of the experiment. Dinitrophenol is known to inhibit secretory movements in tissues where transport depends on oxidative metabolism. It is said to act by uncoupling oxidative phosphorylation which means that respiration continues, sometimes at an accelerated rate, but is no longer capable of forming ATP from inorganic phosphate and ADP. Cyanide and azide which inhibit oxidative metabolism have the same effect on sodium outflow as dinitrophenol. A striking point about these agents is that after the pumping system has been inhibited the fibre can conduct a large number of impulses and neither action potential nor resting potential is much altered in size. Figure 35 shows that after treatment with dinitrophenol sodium ions

74

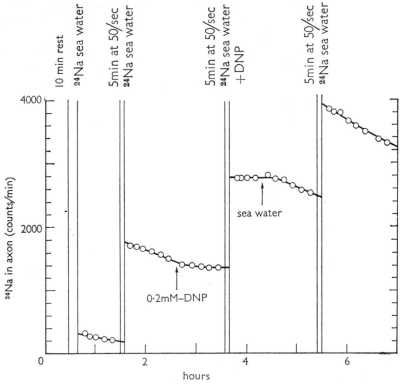

Fig. 35. Effect of 0·2 mM-DNP on sodium entry during stimulation of a squid axon. Temperature 17° C. The abscissa is time and the ordinate gives the amount of ^{24}Na inside the fibre; external ^{24}Na was washed away with a stream of sea water. (From Hodgkin & Keynes, 1955a.)

still moved into the fibre during activity, but that they remained inside and were not extruded until the dinitrophenol was removed.

It is difficult to be sure that all energy yielding reaction have been abolished by cyanide or dinitrophenol but Caldwell's experiments have established quite clearly that giant nerve fibres in which at least 95 per cent of the energy-rich phosphate, arginine phosphate and ATP, has broken down are still capable of conducting action potentials of approximately the normal size.[1] The obvious explanation is that in a large fibre, concentration differences are dissipated very slowly by leakage and that down-hill movements of sodium and potassium provide the immediate source of energy for propagating action potentials. This fits nicely with the perfusion experiments described in Chapter 3, which

1. Caldwell, 1960.

show that membranes filled with isotonic potassium solutions continue to conduct impulses even though nearly all the protoplasm has been removed.

The conclusion from experiments of this kind is that there are two systems in the membrane, one driven by metabolism and responsible for building up concentration differences, the other relatively independent of metabolism and responsible for controlling down-hill movements of sodium and potassium during the action potential (Fig. 36).

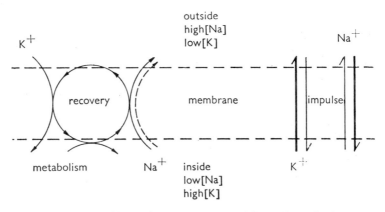

Fig. 36. Diagram illustrating movements of ions through the nerve membrane. The downhill movements which occur during the impulse are shown on the right; uphill movements during recovery are shown on the left. The broken line represents the component of the sodium efflux which is not abolished by removing external potassium ions. (From Hodgkin & Keynes, 1955a.)

The two systems have quite different properties and it is possible to differentiate between them in several ways. Thus the cardiac glycoside, g-strophanthin, which is thought to inhibit pumping by combining with an ATP-splitting enzyme in the membrane has no effect on the action potential.[1] And changes in the external concentrations of divalent ions, which cause radical changes in excitability, have, so far as is known, relatively little effect on the pumping system. The systems also differ in their ionic selectivity, for lithium which can replace sodium in the action potential mechanism is not moved at all effectively by the metabolically driven sodium pump.[2] Another important distinction is that the maximum rate at which the secretory system can move ions is

1. Schatzmann, 1953; Skou, 1957; Caldwell & Keynes, 1959.
2. Keynes & Swan, 1959.

about 50 pmole/cm^2 sec whereas peak movements of up to 10,000 pmole/cm^2 sec occur during the action potential.

It is possible that in other tissues the action potential may be more directly dependent on metabolism than in the squid fibre. For Schoepfle & Bloom (1959) find that the cyanide reduces the action potential of myelinated axons unless these are hyperpolarized. And in muscle the ease with which the action potential can be abolished by fatigue suggests a rather intimate relation between metabolic and electrical events. However, even if metabolism has a direct influence in maintaining the membrane or in generating the permeability changes this would not invalidate the idea that ions are pumped through routes other than those used during the action potential.

The effect of external potassium ions

Having said something about the way in which sodium ions are pumped out of the fibre we must consider whether metabolism is involved in the absorption of potassium ions. At first it was thought that potassium absorption by muscle and nerve was a passive electrical consequence of sodium outflow but there is now evidence, particularly in giant nerve fibres,[1] that potassium uptake may be assisted by a metabolically driven movement, loosely coupled to the outward flow of sodium. In the first place it is found that agents which reduce the outflow of sodium ions have a corresponding effect on potassium uptake. This inhibition takes place without any appreciable change in membrane potential so that it is not a simple electrical consequence of the reduction in sodium transfer. The second piece of evidence is that removal of external potassium causes the outflow of sodium ions to drop, abruptly and reversibly, to about one third of its normal value. This is a rather surprising effect. Sodium is coming from the inside of the fibre where there is always a high concentration of potassium so it is difficult to suppose that removal of the relatively small amount of potassium in sea water shou'² have any direct action on enzymes inside the membrane. The effect does not seem to be electrical in nature, because increases in membrane potential, much greater than those produced by removal of external potassium have little effect on the rate at which sodium ions are extruded.[2]

One rather attractive possibility is that sodium extrusion is coupled to the absorption of potassium in a cyclical manner (Fig. 36). Suppose that potassium ions move into the cell in association with a carrier. Assume that on the inside of the cell, metabolism converts the potassium carrier into a different molecule which has an affinity for sodium but

1. Hodgkin & Keynes, 1955a.   2. Hodgkin & Keynes, 1954.

not for potassium ions. Sodium and its carrier move outwards and the cycle is completed when the carrier, which is now in the sodium form, either reverts or is converted by metabolism into the potassium form.[1] Such a system can be interrupted either by removing external potassium ions or by interfering with metabolism. The coupling with potassium inflow cannot be tight or obligatory because sodium ions continue to be extruded, although at a reduced rate, when all potassium ions are removed from the external medium. There is also evidence that the coupling is not one to one and that 2–3 sodium ions are ejected for each potassium ion absorbed.[2]

Energy-rich phosphate compounds

Although rather little is known about the chemistry of the nerve membrane, it has been possible to find out something about the way in which the secretory system is linked with the respiratory or glycolytic chain. Before considering the recent experiments I must refer to an important biochemical theory which is due to Lipmann (1941). The main function of metabolism is to provide energy, not only for synthesizing new substances but also for performing mechanical work or for moving substances against concentration differences. On Lipmann's theory this energy is provided by the synthesis of certain key substances containing a labile phosphate group. The most important compound is adenosine triphosphate, ATP, but other nucleotides may be involved. Substances like phosphagen, or phosphoenolpyruvate which also contain a labile, energy-rich phosphate group are supposed to act by regenerating adenosine triphosphate from adenosine diphosphate.

There is now much evidence that ATP is frequently used in driving one biochemical reaction at the expense of another, but we cannot yet be equally certain about its importance in linking chemical and physical events in living cells. Experts on muscle are still arguing as to whether hydrolysis of ATP does or does not provide the immediate source of energy for muscular contraction. And there is another more general point. The energy released in splitting ATP, which is about 9000[3] calories per mole, would in many instances seem inconveniently high. It might be thought unlikely that only one type of substance would be involved and that to run a living cell on ATP would be rather like trying to manage the economy of a county with a currency consisting only of one-pound notes. To be more specific, if hydrolysis of ATP forces one ion across a membrane, the energy of the reaction is such that the ion could be driven against an electrochemical potential

1. For further details of this scheme see Glynn, 1958.
2. Caldwell *et al.*, 1960.   3. Burton, 1957.

difference of about 400 mV.[1] This works out very satisfactorily in the stomach where hydrogen ions are transported against an electrochemical potential difference of this order of magnitude, but it is too high for nerve where sodium and potassium must be exchanged against an electrcchemical potential difference of about 120 mV. Transport of 2–3 sodium ions per molecule of ATP split would give a reasonably efficient system and in frog skin, where the electrochemical potential difference is similar to that in nerve, there is evidence of such a relation.[2] But there are other cases in which one seems to need some mechanism for transforming the energy of chemical reactions to even lower levels. For excretory or secretory organs often transport salt against small concentration differences and to do this efficiently hydrolysis of one ATP molecule should result in movement of a large number of ions. Very little seems to be known about this aspect of a cell's economy and it would not be surprising if energy-carrying compounds besides ATP turned out to be important. However, in spite of these doubts, the experiments which we have carried out on giant axons are in good agreement with Lipmann's theory.

The first step, which was taken by Caldwell[3] some years ago, was to study the effects of metabolic inhibitors on the phosphate compounds in the giant axons of *Loligo*. The three main forms of phosphate in the axoplasm are inorganic phosphate, ATP and phosphagen. In the squid, which is a mollusc, the phosphagen is arginine phosphate, not creatine phosphate as it is in vertebrates. If cyanide or dinitrophenol are applied in concentrations which inhibit sodium extrusion, phosphagen breaks down to arginine and inorganic phosphate; and ATP breaks down to adenylic acid (AMP) and inorganic phosphate. On removing cyanide, the ATP and phosphagen are resynthesized. When cyanide is applied, arginine phosphate breaks down first and until its hydrolysis is nearly complete there is little change in ATP. The sodium outflow declines with a time course similar to that of ATP but, as will appear presently, there is evidence to show that the transport system does not operate normally unless both phosphagen and ATP are present.

Injection of energy-rich phosphate compounds

Caldwell's experiments were consistent with the idea that phosphate compounds like ATP or phosphagen provide the energy for working

---

1. This is for all reactants at 1 molar concentration; 500–600 mV might be more appropriate to a living cell.
2. Zerahn, 1956; Leaf and Renshaw, 1957.
3. Caldwell, 1956, 1960.

the sodium pump.[1] In principle this idea can be tested rather simply. All that need be done is to wipe out the store of energy-rich phosphate with cyanide and then to inject ATP or phosphagen. If these substances can drive the pump there should be an immediate increase in sodium efflux. The experiments of Caldwell & Keynes (1957) showed that both compounds were effective and later work[2] proved that their action was shared to varying extents by other compounds containing energy-rich phosphate ($\sim$ P). No effect was obtained from substances not containing $\sim$ P. Seven compounds containing $\sim$ P were tested, namely arginine phosphate, phosphopyruvate, ATP, ADP, guanosine triphosphate, inosine triphosphate and creatine phosphate. Inosine triphosphate had a very slight action and guanosine triphosphate a moderate one. In contrast to arginine phosphate, creatine phosphate (the vertebrate phosphagen) was totally without effect. This is satisfactory since Ennor and his colleagues have shown that creatine phosphate is not handled by the enzyme arginine phosphokinase.[3]

All the compounds which promote an outflow of sodium ions might do so by regenerating ATP by reactions such as

$$\text{I} \quad \text{ADP} + \text{arginine P} = \text{ATP} + \text{arginine} \quad \text{(Arginine phosphokinase)}$$
$$\text{II} \quad \text{ADP} + \text{pyruvate P} = \text{ATP} + \text{pyruvate} \quad \text{(Pyruvate phosphokinase)}$$
$$\text{III} \quad 2\text{ADP} \qquad\qquad = \text{ATP} + \text{AMP} \qquad \text{(Adenylate kinase)}$$

It is assumed that axoplasm contains the necessary enzymes and that a small amount of ADP is left after cyanide poisoning. ATP is formed from ADP by reaction I or II and AMP is converted into ADP by reaction III. As in muscle the overall effect is a conversion of AMP to ATP. Evidence for such reactions is provided by chemical experiments which show that there is a virtually complete conversion of AMP to ATP within five minutes of injecting arginine phosphate or phosphopyruvate into axons poisoned with cyanide.

Figure 37 illustrates the effect of the two phosphagens. It shows the action of cyanide in depressing the outflow of sodium ions, the failure of creatine phosphate to increase the outflow and the large rise produced by arginine phosphate.

ATP had no effect when hydrolysed to AMP and inorganic phosphate, nor did arginine phosphate when broken down to arginine and inorganic phosphate. Another interesting point is that arginine phosphate and ATP were both ineffective when applied externally.

1. For similar evidence in mammalian nerve, see Greengard & Straub, 1959; and in red cells, see Fleckenstein et al., 1956; Whittam, 1958: Hoffman, 1961.
2. Caldwell et al., 1960.
3. Ennor & Morrison, 1958.

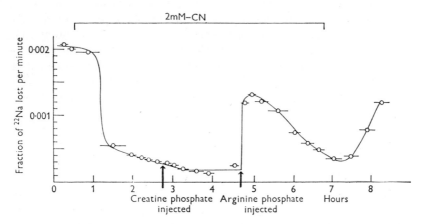

Fig. 37. The effect on the outflow of sodium from an axon poisoned with cyanide of injecting first creatine phosphate and then arginine phosphate. The mean concentrations in the axon immediately after the injections were 15·3 mM– creatine phosphate and 15·8 mM– arginine phosphate. (From Caldwell, Hodgkin, Keynes & Shaw, 1960.)

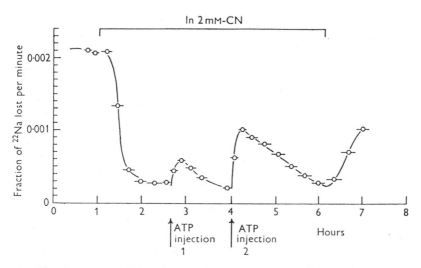

Fig. 38. The effect of injecting two different amounts of ATP into an axon poisoned with cyanide; injection 1 raised the ATP concentration in the axon by 1·2 mM and injection 2 by 6·2 mM. (From Caldwell et al, 1960.)

The action of injected phosphate compounds was transient as would be expected if they are used up in driving ion transport – or in side-reactions. With an injection equivalent to half the total energy-rich phosphate in an unpoisoned axon, the effect lasted for about 30 minutes; with fifteen times this quantity the outflow of sodium remained at a high level for several hours. The maximum outflow did not rise linearly with the quantity injected but in the case of arginine phosphate reached a saturating level of about the same magnitude as that in a normal fibre. As has been reported in other situations, high concentrations of ATP had a depressant effect.

From Figure 38, which gives the effect of injecting two different quantities of ATP, it can be seen that the quantity of sodium ions extruded was roughly proportional to the quantity of ATP injected. Measurements of this kind gave the number of sodium ions extruded for each high-energy phosphate injected as about 0·7 in the case of arginine phosphate and ATP. Since these compounds may break down in the axoplasm before reaching the membrane it is possible that the pumping system uses phosphate bond energy with an efficiency substantially greater than 0·7. In frog skin, Leaf & Renshaw (1957) calculate an $Na/\sim P$ ratio of between 2 and 3 and it may well be that a similar value applies to nerve.

Earlier in this chapter we considered experiments which suggested that there might be a loose coupling between the uptake of potassium and the output of sodium. One piece of evidence was that removal of potassium from the external solution reduced the outflow of sodium to about one-third of its normal value. A possible explanation is that metabolism drives a cycle in which potassium ions are taken up on one limb and sodium ions are extruded on the other. Whatever the explanation, it was plainly important to find out whether injections did restore the normal coupling between sodium and potassium movements. This was done by seeing whether the outflow of sodium after an injection was cut down by removal of external potassium. The answer, which at first may seem rather surprising, was that high concentrations of arginine phosphate and phosphopyruvate restored potassium sensitivity but that none of the other compounds, including ATP, were able to do so.

The action of arginine phosphate is shown in Figure 39. After injecting a large quantity into the poisoned fibre the sodium efflux rose rapidly to a saturating value and remained there for two hours. At first there was evidently a coupled movement, for the sodium outflow was cut down when potassium ions were removed from the external solution. However, the potassium sensitivity was lost fairly rapidly and had

82

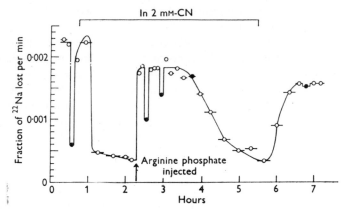

Fig. 39.—Effect of injecting arginine phosphate in restoring a potassium-sensitive sodium efflux to an axon poisoned with cyanide; ● K-free external solution; ○ external solution containing 10 mM-K. The injection raised the concentration of arginine phosphate in the axon by 33 mM. (From Caldwell *et al*, 1960.)

disappeared at the end of the plateau. The decline may be attributed to a loss of arginine phosphate or to a rise in the concentration of arginine or more probably to both.

In a similar experiment with ATP there was no restoration of potassium sensitivity (Fig. 40).

As a corollary to these results it was found that when arginine phosphate was injected into axons poisoned with cyanide it increased the inflow of potassium ions (which had been reduced by cyanide) to about

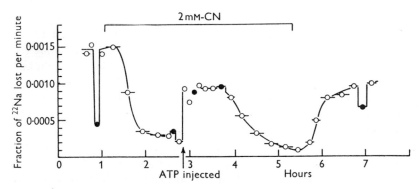

Fig. 40. Failure of ATP to restore a K-sensitive sodium efflux; ● K-free external solution; ○ 10 mM-K. The injection raised the concentration of ATP in the axon by 4·8 mM. (From Caldwell *et al*, 1960.)

83

the same level as in an unpoisoned fibre. ATP produced little or no increase in potassium uptake.

One way of explaining the greater effectiveness of arginine phosphate is to assume that it is directly concerned in handing on phosphate to the membrane. Although this possibility cannot be excluded it runs counter to the standard idea that phosphagen acts by regenerating ATP from ADP. We can reconcile our experiments with the orthodox view by supposing that the pump requires not only the presence of ATP but also that there should be a low concentration of ADP.[1] An alternative statement is that the phosphorylation potential, which is proportional to $\log \frac{[\text{ATP}]}{[\text{ADP}]}$, should be large enough to permit formation of some intermediate which can yield more free energy than ATP. If Z is an intermediate or possibly a carrier and the bond Z–P yields more energy when broken than the terminal bond in ATP, a high $\frac{\text{ATP}}{\text{ADP}}$ ratio would be required to drive the reaction ATP + Z = ADP + ZP in the direction of ZP. On this view arginine phosphate or phosphopyruvate act by regenerating ATP but are more effective because they keep ADP at a low level by the reactions

$$\text{Arg. P} + \text{ADP} = \text{Arg} + \text{ATP}$$
$$\text{Pyruvate P} + \text{ADP} = \text{Pyruvate} + \text{ATP}$$

The results of injecting ADP or arginine into unpoisoned axons were consistent with this idea, since both made the sodium outflow insensitive to removal of potassium.

The function of phosphagens is usually considered to be that of providing a store of energy-rich phosphate which can rapidly resynthesize ATP from ADP. They are present at high concentrations in skeletal muscle and here there are good reasons for believing that they do act as reservoirs of energy. But in nerve where the ionic concentration differences provide a large store of electrical energy the need for a phosphagen is less obvious and it is natural to speculate about its function. The injection experiments suggest that phosphagen might act both as a carrier of energy-rich phosphate and as a buffer which keeps the concentration of ADP at a low level near the membrane. In this connection it is important to remember that the equilibrium constant of the reaction between creatine phosphate and ADP is such that when creatine phosphate and creatine are present at equal concentrations the ratio of [ATP] to [ADP] is about 20.[2] Assuming a similar relation for arginine phosphate it follows that the diffusion gradient of arginine between membrane and mitochondrion is likely to be much greater

1. This hypothesis is due to Dr P. C. Caldwell.
2. Carlson & Siger, 1959.

than that of ADP so that phosphagen should be more important than ATP in carrying energy-rich phosphate through the protoplasm. Such a hypothesis would be in no way inconsistent with the orthodox view that ATP is the immediate link both at the mitochondrion and at the site where energy is needed.

A line of evidence which strongly supports the idea of a close connection between ATP breakdown and ion transport comes from work on the enzymes which catalyse the hydrolysis of ATP. Skou (1957) showed that a particulate preparation obtained from crab nerve contained an ATPase which required both Na and K for its activation and which was inhibited by ouabain, a substance known to interfere with ion transport. An enzyme with similar properties seems to be closely associated with the membrane of red cells and has been studied in preparations of red cell ghosts by Post *et al.* (1960) and by Dunham & Glynn (1961). The inference from these investigations, and from much other work which has not been mentioned, is that phosphorylation of a lipid soluble substance may be an essential step in ion transport.

At present we have little idea as to the nature of the carriers in the membrane, and no real proof of their existence. However, certain experimental clues are beginning to emerge. In a recent paper, Dr & Mrs Hokin (1960) reported that the secretory activity of the salt glands of marine birds involves a 13-fold increase in the rate at which ^{32}P is incorporated into phosphatidic acid and a 7-fold increase in the rate into phosphoinositol, the turnover of phosphorus in other compounds being little affected by making the gland secrete. On the basis of this result the authors propose a scheme in which phosphatidic acid acts as a sodium carrier. Since activity in the salt gland may involve a large increase in the total amount of membrane present – through formation of vesicles, endoplasmic reticulum, proliferations of the surface and so on – it is hard to be sure that their effect may not be a rather unspecific one, related to an increased synthesis of phospholipid. Yet the experiment is clearly an interesting point of departure and it is encouraging that, after so many years of speculation, definite candidates for membrane carriers should at last be appearing in the literature.

Appendix

The physically minded biologist will want to know something further about the mathematical theory of the action potential. The following account which is reprinted with little change from the Proceedings of the Royal Society (1958) gives the basis of the theory which Huxley and I developed for the squid axon.[1]

To describe the change in potassium conductance it is assumed that a path for potassium is formed when four charged particles move to a certain region of the membrane under the influence of the electric field. If n is the probability that a single particle is in the right place, then $g_K = \bar{g}_K n^4$, where $\bar{g}_K$ is the maximum potassium conductance. The value of n is given by

$$\frac{dn}{dt} = \alpha_n(1 - n) - \beta_n n, \tag{1}$$

where α_n and β_n are rate constants which, at a fixed temperature and calcium concentration, depend only on the membrane potential, V. α_n increases and β_n decreases as the inside of the fibre becomes more positive.

For the sodium channel it is assumed that three simultaneous events each of probability m, open the channel to Na and that a single event of probability $(1 - h)$ blocks it. These events need not be specified, but may be thought of as the movement of three activating particles and of one blocking particle to a certain region of the membrane. The probability that there will be three activating particles and no blocking particle is therefore m^3h. Hence $g_{Na} = \bar{g}_{Na} m^3 h$, where $\bar{g}_{Na}$ is the maximum sodium conductance. The values of m and h are given by relations similar to (1), i.e.

$$\frac{dm}{dt} = \alpha_m(1 - m) - \beta_m m, \tag{2}$$

$$\frac{dh}{dt} = \alpha_h(1 - h) - \beta_h h. \tag{3}$$

The α's and β's in these equations depend on temperature, calcium concentration and membrane potential. The effect of making the inside of the fibre more positive is to increase α_m and β_h and to decrease β_m and α_h.

It is relatively simple to apply equations (1), (2) and (3) to the

1. Hodgkin & Huxley, 1952d.

voltage-clamp data. At a fixed voltage the α's and β's are constant so equations (1), (2) and (3) lead to exponential expressions for n, m and h; conductances are then calculated from the relations $g_K = \bar{g}_K n^4$ and $g_{Na} = \bar{g}_{Na} m^3 h$. With values of α and β which change with membrane potential in a consistent manner, a fair though not a perfect fit is obtained. This is illustrated by Figure 29 in which the smooth curves have been calculated and the circles are experimental estimates of the sodium and potassium conductance. The effects of repolarizing the membrane in shutting-off the conductances were taken into account in formulating the equations, and are described by them without any further assumption.

The complete expression for the membrane current density, I, is

$$I = c\frac{\partial V}{\partial t} + (V - V_K)\bar{g}_K n^4 + (V - V_{Na})\bar{g}_{Na} m^3 h + (V - V_L)\bar{g}_L. \tag{4}$$

The first term on the right-hand side is the capacity current, c being the membrane capacity per unit area. The second and third terms give the potassium and sodium currents while the last term, which is relatively unimportant, gives the current carried by other ions, including chloride, through a constant leak conductance $\bar{g}_L$.

If an action potential is elicited over a length of nerve, by applying a short shock to a long metal wire in the axoplasm, there is no longitudinal current and no radial current at any time after the shock. Under these conditions (4) can be simplified by putting $I = 0$ for $t > 0$, the boundary condition being the intial displacement of V. Solutions of this kind have been worked out numerically, or with an automatic computer; the results agree reasonably with the behaviour of a real nerve, as may be seen from Figure 32.

To calculate the form and velocity of the propagated action potential, equations (1) to (4) are used in conjunction with the well-known relation for the current density in a continuous nerve fibre surrounded by a large volume of external fluid, that is

$$I = \frac{a}{2R}\frac{\partial^2 V}{\partial x^2}, \tag{5}$$

where a is the radius of the axoplasm and R is its resistivity; x is the distance along the nerve. In the case of a fibre propagating at constant velocity (θ), x may be replaced by $-\theta t$. Hence

$$\frac{a}{2R\theta^2}\frac{d^2 V}{dt^2} = c\frac{dV}{dt} + (V - V_K)\bar{g}_K n^4 + (V - V_{Na})\bar{g}_{Na} m^3 h + (V - V_L)\bar{g}_L. \tag{6}$$

In this equation, the conduction velocity, θ, is constant, but its value is unknown at the beginning of the computation. The procedure is to guess a value for θ and start a trial solution. It is found that V goes to $\pm\infty$ according to whether θ has been chosen too high or too low. The correct value of θ, which corresponds to the natural velocity of propagation, brings the potential back to its resting value at the end of the run. This procedure can be used until about half-way down the falling phase and gives the velocity to many digits; for the calculation of the final part of the propagated action potential, a different method, based on that used for the situation when $I = 0$, was used by Huxley.

The solution which go to $\pm\infty$ correspond to action potentials which are accelerated or retarded by travelling cathodes or anodes.

An example of a propagated action potential calculated numerically by Huxley is given in Figure 30; it has been checked by Cole and his colleagues and by Huxley (1959) with a digital computer.

List of abbreviations

Adenosine tri, di or monophosphoric acid	ATP, ADP, AMP
Ångstrom unit (10^{-8} centimetre)	Å
Centimetre, square centimetre	cm, cm^2
Dinitrophenol	DNP
Electromotive force	emf
'Energy-rich' phosphate	$\sim P$
Gram	g
Gram-molecule, or gram-ion	mole
Kilogram	kg
Logarithm to base e	ln
Metre	m
Micron (10^{-6} metre)	μ
Microfarad (10^{-6} Farad)	μF
Micromole (10^{-6} mole)	μmole
Milliampere	mA
Millimolar (concentration)	mM
Millivolt	mV
Minute	min
Picomole (10^{-12} mole)	pmole
Picofarad (10^{-12} Farad)	pF
Second	sec
Volt	V

Other symbols are defined in the text; note that F (italics) is used for the Faraday constant, i.e. 96,500 coulombs per mole, and F (as in μF), for the Farad, the unit of electrical capacity.

Bibliography

ABBOTT, B. C., HILL, A. V. & HOWARTH, J. V. 1958. The positive and negative heat production associated with a nerve impulse. *Proc. Roy. Soc. B.* **148**, 149.

ADRIAN, E. D. 1926. The impulses produced by sensory nerve-endings. Parts I and IV. *J. Physiol.* **61**, 49 and **62**, 33.

ADRIAN, E. D. 1928. *The basis of sensation.* Christophers, London.

ADRIAN, E. D. 1932. *The mechanism of nervous action.* Oxford University Press.

ADRIAN, E. D. 1947. *The physical background of perception.* Clarendon Press, Oxford.

ADRIAN, E. D. & ZOTTERMAN, Y. 1926. The impulses produced by sensory nerve-endings. Parts II and III. *J. Physiol.* **61**, 151 and 465.

ADRIAN, R. H. 1956. The effect of internal and external potassium concentration on the membrane potential of frog muscle. *J. Physiol.* **133**, 631.

ARVANITAKI, A. 1938. *Les variations graduées de la polarisation des systèmes excitables.* Hermann & Cie, Paris.

ASANO, T. & HURLBUT, W. P. 1958. Effects of potassium, sodium and azide on the ionic movements that accompany activity in frog nerves. *J. gen. Physiol.* **41**, 1187.

AUBERT, X., FESSARD, A. & KEYNES, R. D. 1961. The thermal events during and after the discharge of the electric organs of *Torpedo* and *Electrophorus*, p. 136 in *Biolectrogenesis.* Elsevier, Amsterdam.

AUBERT, X. & KEYNES, R. D. 1961. Temperature changes in the electric organ of *Electrophorus electricus* during and after its discharge. *J. Physiol.* **158**, 17P.

AUGER, D. 1933. Contribution à l'étude de la propagation de la variation électrique chez les Characées. *C.R. Soc. Biol., Paris*, **113**, 1437.

BAKER, P. F., HODGKIN, A. L. & SHAW, T. I. 1961. Replacement of the protoplasm of a giant nerve fibre with artificial solutions. *Nature, Lond.* **190**, 885.

BAKER, P. F. & SHAW, T. I. 1961. Report for 1960–61. *J. Mar. Biol. Assoc. U.K.* **41**, 855.

BEAR, R. S., SCHMITT, F. O. & YOUNG, J. Z. 1937. The ultrastructure of nerve axoplasm. *Proc. Roy. Soc. B.* **123**, 505.

BERESINA, M. 1932. The resting heat production of nerve. *J. Physiol.* **76**, 170.

BERNSTEIN, J. 1902. Untersuchungen zur Thermodynamik der bioelektrischen Ströme. Erster Theil. *Pflüg. Arch. ges. Physiol.* **92**, 521.

BERNSTEIN, J. 1912. *Elektrobiologie.* Braunschweig: Vieweg.

BERNSTEIN, J. & TSCHERMAK, A. 1906. Untersuchungen zur Thermo-dynamik der bioelektrischen Ströme. Zweiter Teil. Über die Natur der Kette des elektrischen Organs bei *Torpedo. Pflüg. Arch. ges. Physiol.* **112,** 439.

BLINKS, L. R. 1936. The effect of current flow on biolectric potential. III. *Nitella. J. gen. Physiol.* **20,** 229.

BOYLE, P. J. & CONWAY, E. J. 1941. Potassium accumulation in muscle and associated changes. *J. Physiol.* **100,** 1.

BRINK, F., BRONK, D. W., CARLSON, F. D. & CONNELLY, C. M. 1952. The oxygen uptake of active axons. *Cold Spr. Harb. Symp. Quant. Biol.* **17,** 53.

BRONK, D. W. & FERGUSON, L. K. 1935. The nervous control of inter-costal respiration. *Amer. J. Physiol.* **110,** 700.

BURTON, K. 1957. Free energy data of biological interest. Appendix, p. 275, in Krebs & Kornberg, 1957. *Ergebn. Physiol.* **49,** 212.

CALDWELL, P. C. 1956. The effects of certain metabolic inhibitors on the phosphate esters of the squid giant axon. *J. Physiol.* **132,** 35P.

CALDWELL, P. C. 1960. The phosphorus metabolism of squid axons and its relationship to the active transport of sodium. *J. Physiol.* **152,** 545.

CALDWELL, P. C., HODGKIN, A. L., KEYNES, R. D. & SHAW, T. I. 1960. The effects of injecting 'energy-rich' phosphate compounds on the active transport of ions in the giant axons of *Loligo. J. Physiol.* **152,** 561.

CALDWELL, P. C. & KEYNES, R. D. 1957. The utilization of phosphate bond energy for sodium extrusion from giant axons. *J. Physiol.* **137,** 12P.

CALDWELL, P. C. & KEYNES, R. D. 1959. The effect of ouabain on the efflux of sodium from a squid giant axon. *J. Physiol.* **148,** 8P.

CALDWELL, P. C. & KEYNES, R. D. 1960. The permeability of the squid giant axon to radioactive potassium and chloride ions. *J. Physiol.* **154,** 177.

CARLSON, F. D. & SIGER, A. 1959. The creatine phosphoryltransfer reaction in iodoacetate-poisoned muscle. *J. gen. Physiol.* **43,** 301.

COLE, K. S. 1949. Dynamic electrical characteristics of the squid axon membrane. *Arch. Sci. physiol.* **3,** 253.

COLE, K. S. 1955. Ions, potentials and the nerve impulse. In *Electrochemistry in biology and medicine,* p. 121. Wiley, New York.

COLE, K. S., ANTOSIEWICZ, A. & RABINOWITZ, P. 1955. Automatic computation of nerve excitation. *J. Soc. Indust. Appl. Math.* **3,** 153.

COLE, K. S. & CURTIS, H. J. 1938. Electric impedance of *Nitella* during activity. *J. gen. Physiol.* **22,** 37.

COLE, K. S. & CURTIS, H. J. 1939. Electric impedance of the squid giant axon during activity. *J. gen. Physiol.* **22,** 649.

COLE, K. S. & HODGKIN, A. L. 1939. Membrane and protoplasm resistance in the squid giant axon. *J. gen. Physiol.* **22,** 671.

CONNELLY, C. M. 1959. Recovery processes and metabolism of nerve, p. 475 in *Biophysical Science*, published in *Rev. Modern Physics*, Vol. 31 and by Wiley, New York.

CONNELLY, C. M. & CRANEFIELD, P. F. 1953. The oxygen consumption of the stellar nerve of the squid (*Loligo pealii*). *XIX Int. Physiol. Congr.*, *Montreal, Abstracts of Communications*, p. 276.

CONWAY, E. J. 1957. Nature and significance of concentration relations of potassium and sodium ions in skeletal muscle. *Physiol. Rev.* **37**, 84.

CURTIS, H. J. & COLE, K. S. 1938. Transverse electric impedance of the squid giant axon. *J. gen. Physiol.* **21**, 757.

CURTIS, H. J. & COLE, K. S. 1940. Membrane action potentials from the squid giant axon. *J. cell. comp. Physiol.* **15**, 147.

CURTIS, H. J. & COLE, K. S. 1942. Membrane resting and action potentials from the squid giant axon. *J. cell. comp. Physiol.* **19**, 135.

DALTON, J. C. 1958. Effects of external ions on membrane potentials of a lobster giant axon. *J. gen. Physiol.* **41**, 529.

DAVSON, H. & DANIELLI, J. F. 1943. *The permeability of natural membranes* Cambridge University Press.

DEAN, R. B. 1941. Theories of electrolyte equilibrium in muscle. *Biol. Symp.* **3**, 331.

DEL CASTILLO, J. & KATZ, B. 1956. Biophysical aspects of neuro-muscular transmission. *Progr. Biophys.* **6**, 121.

DEL CASTILLO, J. & MOORE, J. W. 1959. On increasing the velocity of a nerve impulse. *J. Physiol.* **148**, 665.

DODGE, F. A. & FRANKENHAEUSER, B. 1958. Membrane currents in isolated frog nerve fibre under voltage clamp conditions. *J. Physiol.* **143**, 76.

DODGE, F. A. & FRANKENHAEUSER, B. 1959. Sodium currents in the myelinated nerve fibre of *Xenopus laevis* investigated with the voltage clamp technique. *J. Physiol.* **148**, 188.

DONALDSON, H. H. & HOKE, G. W. 1905. On the areas of the axis cylinder and medullary sheath as seen in cross sections of the spinal nerves of vertebrates. *J. comp. Neurol. & Psychol.* **15**, 1.

DRAPER, M. H. & WEIDMANN, S. 1951. Cardiac resting and action potentials recorded with an intracellular electrode. *J. Physiol.* **115**, 74.

DUNHAM, E. T. & GLYNN, I. M. 1961. Adenosinetriphosphatase activity and the active movements of alkali metal ions. *J. Physiol.* **156**, 274.

ENNOR, A. H. & MORRISON, J. F. 1958. Biochemistry of the phosphagens and related guanidines. *Physiol. Rev.* **38**, 631.

ERLANGER, J. & BLAIR, E. A. 1934. Manifestations of segmentation in myelinated axons. *Amer. J. Physiol.* **110**, 287.

ERLANGER, J. & BLAIR, E. A. 1938. The action of isotonic, salt-free solutions on conductance in medullated nerve fibres. *Amer. J. Physiol.* **124**, 341.

ERLANGER, J. & GASSER, H. S. 1937. *Electrical signs of nervous activity.* Philadelphia: Univ. of Pennsylvania Press.

FATT, P. 1961. Transverse impedance measurement of striated muscle. *J. Physiol.* **157**, 10P.

FATT, P. & GINSBORG, B. L. 1958. The ionic requirements for the production of action potentials in crustacean muscle fibres. *J. Physiol.* **142**, 516.

FATT, P. & KATZ, B. 1951. An analysis of the end-plate potential recorded with an intra-cellular electrode. J. *Physiol.* **115**, 320.

FATT, P. & KATZ, B. 1953. The electrical properties of crustacean muscle fibres. *J. Physiol.* **120**, 171.

FESSARD, A. 1936. *Propriétés rythmiques de la matière vivante* II. Hermann & Cie, Paris.

FESSARD, A. 1946. Some basic aspects of the activity of electric plates. *Ann. N. Y. Acad. Sci.* **47**, 501.

FINEAN, J. B. 1957. The molecular structure of nerve myelin and its significance in relation to the nerve 'membrane', p. 52 of *Metabolism of the nervous system.* Pergamon Press, London.

FITZHUGH, R. 1961. Impulses and physiological states in theoretical models of nerve membrane. *Biophys. J.* **1**, 445.

FLECKENSTEIN, A., GERLACH, E. & JANKE, J. 1956. Phosphorylierung und aktiver Kationentransport. *Schweiz. med. wochenschrift.* **86**, 1041.

FRANKENHAEUSER, B. 1959. Steady state inactivation of sodium permeability in myelinated nerve fibres of *Xenopus laevis. J. Physiol.* **148**, 671.

FRANKENHAEUSER, B. 1960. Quantitative description of sodium currents in myelinated nerve fibres of *Xenopus laevis. J. Physiol.* **151**, 491.

FRANKENHAEUSER, B. & HODGKIN, A. L. 1956. The after-effects of impulses in the giant nerve fibres of *Loligo. J. Physiol.* **131**, 341.

FRANKENHAEUSER, B. & HODGKIN, A. L. 1957. The action of calcium on the electrical properties of squid axons. *J. Physiol.* **137**, 218.

FRAZIER, H. S. & KEYNES, R. D. 1959. The effect of metabolic inhibitors on the sodium fluxes in sodium-loaded frog sartorius muscle. *J. Physiol.* **148**, 362.

FRITSCH, G. 1887. *Die elektrische Fische.* vol. 1, p. 4, von Veit, Leipzig.

FULTON, J. F. 1952. *The frontal lobes and human behaviour.* Sherrington lectures II. University Press of Liverpool.

GAFFEY, C. T. & MULLINS, L. J. 1958. Ion fluxes during the action potential in *Chara. J. Physiol.* **144**, 505.

GASSER, H. S. & GRUNDFEST, H. 1936. Action and excitability in mammalian A fibres. *Amer. J. Physiol.* **117**, 113.

GASSER, H. S. & GRUNDFEST, H. 1939. Axon diameters in relation to the spike dimensions and the conduction velocity in mammalian A fibres. *Amer. J. Physiol.* **127**, 393.

93

GEREN, B. B. 1954. The formation from the Schwann cell surface of myelin in the peripheral nerves of chick embryos. *Expt. cell. Res.* **7**, 558.

GEREN, B. B. & SCHMITT, F. O. 1954. The structure of the Schwann cell and its relation to the axon in certain invertebrate nerve fibres. *Proc. Nat. Acad. Sci. Wash.* **40**, 863.

GLYNN, I. M. 1957. The ionic permeability of the red cell membrane. *Progr. Biophysics.* **8**, 241.

GORDON, H. T. & WELSH, J. H. 1948. The role of ions in axon surface reactions to toxic organic compounds. *J. cell. comp. Physiol.* **31**, 395.

GORTER, E. & GRENDEL, F. 1925. On bimolecular layers of lipoids on the chromocytes of the blood. *J. exp. Med.* **41**, 439.

GOTCH, F. & BURCH, G. J. 1899. The electrical response of nerve to two stimuli. *J. Physiol.* **24**, 410.

GOTCH, F. & HORSLEY, V. 1891. On the mammalian nervous system, its functions, and their localisation determined by an electrical method. *Philos. Trans. B.* 1891, p. 267.

GRANIT, R. 1955. *Receptors and sensory perception.* Yale University Press.

GRAY, J. A. B. 1959. Initiation of impulses at receptors. Chapter 4. *Hdbk. of Physiol. Section* 1. *Neurophysiology.* Vol. 1, p. 123. Williams & Wilkins, Baltimore.

GREENGARD, P. & STRAUB, R. W. 1959. Effect of frequency of electrical stimulation on the concentration of intermediary metabolites in mammalian non-myelinated fibres. *J. Physiol.* **148**, 353.

GRUNDFEST, H. 1957. Electrical inexcitability of synapses and some consequences in the central nervous system. *Physiol. Rev.* **37**, 337.

GRUNDFEST, H. & NACHMANSOHN, D. 1950. Increased sodium entry into squid giant axons at high frequencies and during reversible inactivation of cholinesterase. *Fed. Proc.* **9**, 53.

HAGIWARA, S. & OOMURA, Y. 1958. The critical depolarization for the spike in the squid giant axon. *Jap. J. Physiol.* **8**, 234.

HARTLINE, H. K. 1934. Intensity and duration in the excitation of single photoreceptor units. *J. cell. comp. Physiol.* **5**, 229.

HERMANN, L. 1899. Zur Theorie der Erregungsleitung und der elektrischen Erregung. *Pflüg. Arch.* **75**, 574.

HILL, Λ. V. 1932a. *Chemical wave transmission in nerve.* Cambridge University Press.

HILL, A. V. 1932b. A closer analysis of the heat production of nerve. *Proc. Roy. Soc. B.* **111**, 106.

HINKE, J. A. M. 1961. The measurement of sodium and potassium activities in the squid axon by means of cation-selective glass micro-electrodes. *J. Physiol.* **156**, 314.

HODGKIN, A. L. 1937. Evidence for electrical transmission in nerve. Parts I & II. *J. Physiol.* **90**, 183 and 211.

HODGKIN, A. L. 1938. The subthreshold potentials in a crustacean nerve fibre. *Proc. Roy. Soc. B.* **126**, 87.

HODGKIN, A. L. 1939. The relation between conduction velocity and the electrical resistance outside a nerve fibre. *J. Physiol.* **94**, 560.

HODGKIN, A. L. 1948. The local electric changes associated with repetitive action in a non-medullated axon. *J. Physiol.* **107**, 165.

HODGKIN, A. L. 1951. The ionic basis of electrical activity in nerve and muscle. *Biol. Rev.* **26**, 339.

HODGKIN, A. L. 1954. A note on conduction velocity. *J. Physiol.* **125**, 221.

HODGKIN, A. L. 1958. Ionic movements and electrical activity in giant, nerve fibres. *Proc. Roy. Soc. B.* **148**, 1.

HODGKIN, A. L. & HOROWICZ, P. 1959a. Movements of Na and K in single muscle fibres. *J. Physiol.* **145**, 405.

HODGKIN, A. L. & HOROWICZ, P. 1959b. The influence of potassium and chloride ions on the membrane potential of single muscle fibres. *J. Physiol.* **148**, 127.

HODGKIN, A. L. & HUXLEY, A. F. 1939. Action potentials recorded from inside a nerve fibre. *Nature, Lond.,* **144**, 710.

HODGKIN, A. L. & HUXLEY, A. F. 1945. Resting and action potentials in single nerve fibres. *J. Physiol.* **104**, 176.

HODGKIN, A. L. & HUXLEY, A. F. 1947. Potassium leakage from an active nerve fibre. *J. Physiol.* **106**, 341.

HODGKIN, A. L. & HUXLEY, A. F. 1952a. Currents carried by sodium and potassium ions through the membrane of the giant axon of *Loligo. J. Physiol.* **116**, 449.

HODGKIN, A. L. & HUXLEY, A. F. 1952b. The components of membrane conductance in the giant axon of *Loligo. J. Physiol.* **116**, 473.

HODGKIN, A. L. & HUXLEY, A. F. 1952c. The dual effect of membrane potential on sodium conductance in the giant axon of *Loligo. J. Physiol.* **116**, 497.

HODGKIN, A. L. & HUXLEY, A. F. 1952d. A quantitative description of membrane current and its application to conduction and excitation in nerve. *J. Physiol.* **117**, 500.

HODGKIN, A. L. & HUXLEY, A. F. 1953. Movement of radioactive potassium and membrane current in a giant axon. *J. Physiol.* **121**, 403.

HODGKIN, A. L., HUXLEY, A. F. & KATZ, B. 1952. Measurement of current-voltage relations in the membrane of the giant axon of *Loligo. J. Physiol.* **116**, 424.

HODGKIN, A. L., & KATZ, B. 1949. The effect of sodium ions on the electrical activity of the giant axon of the squid. *J. Physiol.* **108**, 37.

HODGKIN, A. L. & KEYNES, R. D. 1953. The mobility and diffusion coefficient of potassium in giant axons from *Sepia. J. Physiol.* **119**, 513.

HODGKIN, A. L. & KEYNES, R. D. 1954. Movements of cations during recovery in nerve. *Symp. Soc. Exp. Biol.* **8**, 423.

HODGKIN, A. L. & KEYNES, R. D. 1955a. Active transport of cations in giant axons from *Sepia* and *Loligo. J. Physiol.* **128**, 28.

HODGKIN, A. L. & KEYNES, R. D. 1955b. The potassium permeability of a giant nerve fibre. *J. Physiol.* **128**, 61.

HODGKIN, A. L. & KEYNES, R. D. 1956. Experiments on the injection of substances into squid giant axons by means of a microsyringe. *J. Physiol.* **131**, 592.

HODGKIN, A. L. & KEYNES, R. D. 1957. Movements of labelled calcium in squid giant axons. *J. Physiol.* **138**, 253.

HODLER, J., STÄMPFLI, R. & TASAKI, I. 1951 Über die Wirkung internodaler Abkhülung auf die Erregungsleitung in der isolierten markhaltigen Nervenfaser des Frosches. *Pflüg. Arch. ges. Physiol.* **253**, 380.

HODLER, J., STÄMPFLI, R. & TASAKI, I. 1952. Rôle of the potential wave spreading along myelinated fibre in excitation and conduction. *Amer. J. Physiol.* **170**, 375.

HOFFMAN, J. F. 1961. Molecular mechanism of active cation transport, in Biophysics of Physiological and Pharmacological actions, p. 3. Publication No. 69 of the Amer. Assoc. for the Advancement of Science. Washington, D.C.

HOKIN, L. E. & HOKIN, Mabel R. 1960. Studies on the carrier function of phosphatidic acid in sodium transport. I. The turnover of phosphatidic acid and phosphoinositide in the avian salt gland on stimulation of secretion. *J. gen. Physiol.* **44**, 61.

HOLMES, W., PUMPHREY, R. J. & YOUNG, J. Z. 1942. The structure and conduction velocity of the medullated nerve-fibres of prawns. *J. exp. Biol.* **18**, 50.

HURSH, J. B. 1939. Conduction velocity and diameter of nerve fibres. *Amer. J. Physiol.* **127**, 131.

HUXLEY, A. F. 1959. Ion movements during nerve activity. *Ann. N.Y. Acad. Sci.* **81**, 221.

HUXLEY, A. F. & STÄMPFLI, R. 1949a. Evidence for saltatory conduction in peripheral myelinated nerve-fibres. *J. Physiol.* **108**, 315.

HUXLEY, A. F. & STÄMPFLI, R. 1949b. Saltatory transmission of the nervous impulse. *Arch. Sci. physiol.* **3**, 435.

HUXLEY, A. F. & STÄMPFLI, R. 1951a. Direct determination of membrane resting potential and action potential in single myelinated nerve fibres. *J. Physiol.* **112**, 476.

HUXLEY, A. F. & STÄMPFLI, R. 1951b. Effect of potassium and sodium on resting and action potentials of single myelinated nerve fibres. *J. Physiol.* **112**, 496.

KATO, G. 1934. *The microphysiology of nerve.* Maruzen, Tokyo.

KATO, G. 1936. On the excitation, conduction and narcotisation of single nerve fibres. *Cold. Spr. Harb. Symp. quant. Biol.* **4**, 202.

KATZ, B. 1942. Impedance changes in frog's muscle associated with electrotonic and 'end plate' potentials. *J. Neurophysiol.* **5**, 169.

KATZ, B. 1948. The electrical properties of the muscle fibre membrane. *Proc. Roy. Soc. B.* **135**, 506.

KATZ, B. 1960. Book review in *Perspectives in Biology and Medicine.* Vol. III, p. 563.

KATZ, B. 1961. How cells communicate. *Scientific American.* September 1961, p. 209.

KATZ, B. & SCHMITT, O. H. 1940. Electric interaction between two adjacent nerve fibres. *J. Physiol.* **97**, 471.

KATZ, B. & SCHMITT, O. H. 1942. A note on interaction between nerve fibres. *J. Physiol.* **100**, 369.

KEYNES, R. D. 1949. The movements of radioactive ions in resting and stimulated nerve. *Arch. Sci. physiol.* **3**, 165.

KEYNES, R. D. 1951a. The leakage of radioactive potassium from stimulated nerve. *J. Physiol.* **113**, 99.

KEYNES, R. D. 1951b. The ionic movements during nervous activity. *J. Physiol.* **114**, 119.

KEYNES, R. D. 1956. The generation of electricity by fishes. *Endeavour,* **15**, 215.

KEYNES, R. D. & LEWIS, P. R. 1951. The sodium and potassium content of cephalopod nerve fibres. *J. Physiol.* **114**, 151.

KEYNES, R. D. & LEWIS, P. R. 1956. The intracellular calcium contents of some invertebrate nerves. *J. Physiol.* **134**, 399.

KEYNES, R. D. & SWAN, R. C. 1959. The permeability of frog muscle fibres to lithium ions. *J. Physiol.* **147**, 626.

KOECHLIN, B. A. 1955. On the chemical composition of the axoplasm of squid giant nerve fibres with particular reference to its ion pattern. *J. biophys. biochem. Cytol.* **1**, 511.

KREBS, H. A. & KORNBERG, H. L. 1957. Energy transformations in living matter. *Ergebn. Physiol.* **49**, 212.

LEAF, A. & RENSHAW, A. 1957. Ion transport and respiration of isolated frog skin. *Biochem. J.* **65**, 82.

LEWIS, P. R. 1952. The free amino-acids of invertebrate nerve. *Biochem. J.* **52**, 330.

LILLIE, R. S. 1925. Factors affecting transmission and recovery in the passive iron nerve model. *J. gen. Physiol.* **7**, 473.

LING, G. & GERARD, R. W. 1949. The normal membrane potential of frog sartorius fibres. *J. cell. comp. Physiol.* **34**, 383.

LIPMANN, F. 1941. Metabolic generation and utilization of phosphate bond energy. *Adv. Enzymol.* **1**, 99.

LISSMANN, H. W. 1961. Ecological studies on gymnotids, p. 223 in *Bioelectrogenesis.* Elsevier, Amsterdam.

LORENTE DE NÓ, R. 1949. On the effect of certain quaternary ammonium ions upon frog nerve. *J. cell. comp. Physiol.* **33**, Supplement.

LUCAS, K. 1917. *The conduction of the nervous impulse.* Longmans, London. (Revised by E. D. Adrian.)

LUSSIER, J. J. & RUSHTON, W. A. H. 1952. The excitability of a single fibre in a nerve trunk. *J. Physiol.* 117, 87.

LÜTTGAU, H. C. 1958. Die Wirkung von Guanidinhydrochlorid auf die Erregungsprozesse an isolierten markhaltigen Nervenfasern. *Pflüg. Arch. ges. Physiol.* 267, 331.

MAIZELS, M. 1951. Factors in the active transport of cations. *J. Physiol.* 112, 59.

MAIZELS, M. 1954. Active cation transport in erythrocytes. *Symp. Soc. Exp. Biol.* 8, 202.

MARMONT, G. 1949. Studies on the axon membrane. I. A new method. *J. cell. comp. Physiol.* 34, 351.

MATTHEWS, B. H. C. 1933. Nerve endings in mammalian muscle. *J. Physiol.* 78, 1.

MILLER, W. H., RATLIFF, F. & HARTLINE, H. K. 1961. How cells receive stimuli. *Scientific American.* September 1961, p. 223.

MOORE, J. W. & COLE, K. S. 1960. Resting and action potentials of the squid axon *in viva. J. gen Physiol.* 43, 961.

NACHMANSOHN, D. 1959. *Chemical and molecular basis of nerve activity.* Academic Press, New York.

NASTUK, W. L. & HODGKIN, A. L. 1950. The electrical activity of single muscle fibres. *J. cell. comp. Physiol.* 35, 39.

OIKAWA, T., SPYROPOULOS, C. S., TASAKI, I. & TEORELL, T. 1961. Methods for perfusing the giant axon of *Loligo pealii. Acta physiol. scand.* 52, 195.

OSTERHOUT, W. J. V. & HILL, S. E. 1930. Salt bridges and negative variations. *J. gen. Physiol.* 13, 547.

OVERTON, E. 1902. Beiträge zur allgemeinen Muskel- und Nervenphysiologie. *Pflüg. Arch. ges. Physiol.* 92, 346.

PARPART, A. K. & BALLENTINE, R. 1952. Molecular anatomy of the red cell membrane, in *Trends in Physiology and Biochemistry,* p. 135, ed. E. S. G. Barron. Academic Press, New York.

PATTON, H. D. 1960. Chapter 2 in *Medical physiology and biophysics.* Edited by T. C. Ruch and J. F. Fulton. W. B. Saunders, Philadelphia and London.

POST, R. L., MERRITT, C. R., KINSOLVING, C. R. & ALBRIGHT, C. D., 1960. Membrane adenosinetriphosphatase as a participant in the active transport of sodium and potassium in the human erythrocyte. *J. Biol. Chem.* 235, 1796.

ROBERTSON, J. D. 1957. New observations on the ultrastructure of the membranes of frog peripheral nerve fibres. *J. biophys. biochem. Cytol.* 3, 1043.

ROBERTSON, J. D. 1958. Structural alterations in nerve fibres produced by hypotonic and hypertonic solutions. *J. biophys. biochem. Cytol.* **4,** 349.

ROBERTSON, J. D. 1960a. The molecular structure and contact relationships of cell membranes. *Progr. Biophys.* **10,** 343.

ROBERTSON, J. D. 1960b. Myelinating and non-myelinating nerve fibres during development: a new component of the endoplasmic reticulum of Schwann cells. *J. Physiol.* **153,** 40P.

ROTHENBERG, M. A. 1950. Studies on permeability in relation to nerve function. II. Ionic movements across axonal membranes. *Biochem. biophys. acta,* **4,** 96.

RUSHTON, W. A. H. 1951. A theory of the effects of fibre size in medullated nerve. *J. Physiol.* **115,** 101.

SANDERS, F. K. 1948. The thickness of the myelin sheaths of normal and regenerating peripheral nerve fibres. *Proc. Roy. Soc. B.* **135,** 323.

SCHATZMANN, H. J. 1953. Herzglykoside als Hemmstoffe für den aktiven Kalium- und Natriumtransport durch die Erythrocytenmembran. *Helv. Physiol. Acta,* **11,** 346.   */0 9 9 5 5*

SCHMITT, F. O. 1959. Molecular organisation of the nerve fibre, p. 455 in Biophysical Science published in *Rev. Modern Physics,* vol. 31 and by Wiley, New York.

SCHMITT, F. O. & GESCHWIND, N. 1957. The axon surface. *Progr. Biophys.* **8,** 165.

SCHOEPFLE, G. M. & BLOOM, F. E. 1959. Effects of cyanide and dinitrophenol on membrane properties of single nerve fibres. *Amer. J. Physiol.* **197,** 1131.

SCRIBONIUS LARGUS (1st century A.D.) Compositiones. Chapters 11, 99 & 162. Edit. G. Helmreich 1887; Teubner, Leipzig quoted by Fulton (1952) and Keynes (1956).

SHANES, A. M. 1951. Factors in nerve functioning. *Fed. Proc.* **10,** 611.

SHANES, A. M. 1954. Effect of temperature on potassium liberation during nerve activity. *Amer. J. Physiol.* **177,** 377.

SHANES, A. M. 1958. Electrochemical aspects of physiological and pharmacological action in excitable cells. *Pharmacol. Rev.* **10,** 59.

SHANES, A. M. & BERMAN, M. D. 1955. Kinetics of ion movement in the squid giant axon. *J. gen. Physiol.* **39,** 279.

SHERRINGTON, C. S. 1906. *The integrative action of the nervous system.* Yale University Press, New Haven and London.

SKOU, J. C. 1957. The influence of some cations on an adenosinetriphosphatase from peripheral nerves. *Biochem. biophys. acta,* **23,** 394.

STÄMPFLI, R. 1952. Bau und Funktion isolierter markhaltiger Nervenfasern. *Ergebn. Physiol.* **47,** 70.

STEINBACH, H. B. 1941. Chloride in the giant axons of the squid. *J. cell. comp. Physiol.* **17,** 57.

STEINBACH, H. B. & SPIEGELMAN, S. 1943. The sodium and potassium balance in squid axoplasm. *J. cell. comp. Physiol.* **22**, 187.

STEINDORFF, G. 1913. Das Grab des Ti. Plates 113, 114, Vol. 2. Veröffentlichungen der Ernst von Sieglin Expedition in Ägypten. Hinrich, Leipzig.

TASAKI, I. 1939a. Electric stimulation and the excitatory process in the nerve fibre. *Amer. J. Physiol.* **125**, 380.

TASAKI, I. 1939b. The electro-saltatory transmision of the nerve impulse and the effect of narcosis upon the nerve fibre. *Amer. J. Physiol.* **127**, 211.

TASAKI, I. 1953. *Nervous transmission.* Thomas, Springfield.

TASAKI, I. 1955. New measurements of the capacity and the resistance of the myelin sheath and the nodal membrane of the isolated frog nerve fibre. *Amer. J. Physiol.* **181**, 639.

TASAKI, I. 1959. Conduction of the nerve impulse. Chapter 3 *Hdbk. of Physiol. Section 1 Neurophysiology,* Vol. 1, p. 75. Williams & Wilkins, Baltimore.

TASAKI, I. & MIZUGUCHI, K. 1948. Response of single Ranvier nodes to electrical stimuli. *J. Neurophysiol.* **11**, 295.

TASAKI, I. & MIZUGUCHI, K. 1949. The changes in the electric impedance during activity and the effects of alkaloids and polarization upon the bioelectric processes in the myelinated nerve fibre. *Biochem. biophys. acta,* **3**, 484.

TASAKI, I. & TAKEUCHI, T. 1941. Der am Ranvierschen Knoten entstehende Aktionsstrom und seine Bedeutung für die Erregungsleitung. *Pflüg. Arch. ges. Physiol.* **244**, 696.

TASAKI, I. & TAKEUCHI, T. 1942. Weitere Studien über den Aktionsstrom der markhaltigen Nervenfaser und über die elektrosaltatorische Übertragung des Nervenimpulses. *Pflüg. Arch. ges. Physiol.* **245**, 764.

THIES, R. E. 1957. Electrical recording in the living squid. *Biol Bull.,* Wood's Hole, **113**, 333.

THOMPSON, D'ARCY, W. 1947. *A glossary of Greek fishes.* Oxford University Press.

USSING, H. H. 1959. The alkali metal ions in isolated systems and tissues. Part I of *'The alkali metal ions in Biology'. Handb. exp. Pharmakol.* **13**. Springer, Berlin.

VOLTA, A. 1800. On the electricity excited by the mere contact of conducting substances of different kinds. In a letter from Alexander Volta, F.R.S., Professor of Natural Philosophy in the University of Pavia to the Rt. Hon. Sir Joseph Banks, K.B., P.R.S. *Philos. Trans.* **90**, 403.

WEDDELL, G., PALMER, Elizabeth & PALLIE, W. 1955. Nerve endings in mammalian skin. *Biol. Rev.* **30**, 159.

WEIDMANN, S. 1951. Electrical characteristics of *Sepia* axons. *J. Physiol.* **114**, 372.

WHITTAM, R. 1958. Potassium movements and ATP in human red cells. *J. Physiol.* **140,** 479.

YOUNG, J. Z. 1936a. The giant nerve fibres and epistellar body of cephalopods. *Quart. J. Micr. Sci.,* **78,** 367.
YOUNG, J. Z. 1936b. Structure of nerve fibres and synapses in some invertebrates. *Cold Spr. Harb. Symp. Quant. Biol.* **4,** 1.
YOUNG, J. Z. 1938. The functioning of the giant nerve fibres of the squid. *J. exp. Biol.* **15,** 170.

ZERAHN, K. 1956. Oxygen consumption and active sodium transport in the isolated and short-circuited frog skin. *Acta physiol. scand.* **36,** 300.

Author Index

Subject Index

MT

FEI